ATOMS, MOLECULES
and
CHEMICAL CHANGE

PRENTICE-HALL CHEMISTRY SERIES

KENNETH S. PITZER, EDITOR

Atoms, Molecules

and

Chemical Change

ERNEST GRUNWALD

Professor of Chemistry
The Florida State University

RUSSELL H. JOHNSEN

Associate Professor of Chemistry,
Chairman of Physical Science for General Education
The Florida State University

PRENTICE-HALL, INC.
Englewood Cliffs, N. J.

Preface

THIS BOOK is an introduction to chemistry, intended for non-science majors, which emphasizes the structure of matter and the chemical consequences of that structure. It is the result of a general education program in the physical sciences that has been developing for some years at Florida State University. Originally the students were asked to take introductory courses in one or two of the physical sciences. However, this program fell into disfavor because the introductory courses were necessarily designed for science majors and were too technical and too narrow in scope for general education. To overcome these difficulties a one-year integrated physical science course was instituted. But, after more than a decade of experimentation with this course, neither the faculty nor the students were unreservedly enthusiastic about the result. It seemed that one year just was not enough time in which to cover the multiplicity of subjects, ranging from physics to geology. The course suffered from a lack of depth, and this seemed inexcusable, particularly in the physical sciences.

We therefore decided to try a program in which we would sacrifice some breadth for the sake of greater depth. As a result a logically complete, one-semester course was developed for each of the sciences: physics, chemistry, astronomy, meteorology, and geology. The physical science requirement was then changed so that each student not majoring in science elected the special course in either physics or chemistry for his first semester, and astronomy, meteorology, or geology for his second semester. This plan leaves a desirable degree of choice open to the students, familiarizes the student with both a laboratory science and a field science, and permits a greater depth of treatment in the subjects the student elects.

Although *not* intended for a pre-professional course in chemistry, this text does not lack logical rigor. Emphasis is placed on fundamental ideas, without an excessive amount of time being spent on drill in their application. One of our aims is that the student might acquire a feeling for the spirit in which chemical knowledge is developed, and thus be motivated to maintain an active interest in science.

Our classes are extraordinarily heterogeneous, in terms of both preparation and interests. Students are drawn from all the professional schools as well as the College of Arts and Sciences. About half of our students have had high school chemistry, and perhaps one-third have quite limited mathematical ability. The course and consequently this book is therefore largely non-mathematical, and contains very little of the descriptive material which is usually emphasized in most high school courses. The unifying theme—the structure of matter and the chemical consequences of that structure—was chosen because it enabled us to present chemistry from a point of view which is more advanced than that of most high school courses, and yet to develop the subject in such a way that those of our students who have not had previous schooling in chemistry would not be at a disadvantage. This theme enables us to discuss some inspiring discoveries and examples of the human mind at work. Moreover, the basic ideas can be taught within the short span of a single semester.

The theme of the structure of matter is developed in a partly historical and partly logical sequence so that the degree of difficulty increases gradually throughout the book. It is felt that to cover this material adequately (supplemented by lecture demonstrations and discussion), three to five semester-hours are required. The authors are currently utilizing three semester-hours.

Many topics which are usually treated in a general chemistry course are of necessity omitted, such as oxidation-reduction, chemical equilibrium, and the colligative properties of solutions. Stoichiometric calculations have been de-emphasized, except where they serve to illustrate a broader concept.

Our main interest in writing this book is to teach chemistry. But we have not overlooked the fact that this course is part of a general education program and have, therefore, tried to emphasize the "liberal" aspect of science. To quote Charles Frankel: "Science is an example par excellence of a liberal art—a deliberate selective recording of experience, which releases men from the narrowness and urgency of routine affairs, carries them beyond accidents and limitations of their lives, and makes it possible for their commerce with the world to have scope, order, and systematic consequences. It has been used as an instrument of . . . war, but its primary function is more humane and, as it were, aesthetic. And its relationship to practice is the relation of any fine and liberating art—it carries men beyond the foreground of their experience, and enlarges the dimensions of human choice by acquainting men with the alternative possibilities of things. Quite apart from its technological applications, it represents, to use an old philosophical expression, a 'final good'—something which has its own inner dynamism, goes its own way, and can give stability and direction to the rest of our lives."*

Finally, we acknowledge our appreciation to the following sources for permission to reproduce photographs: Brown Brothers, pp. 26, 35, 38, 44, 92, 105, 208, 225; Culver Service, pp. 121, 222; M. Kasha, p. 139; British Information Services, p. 97.

E. G.

Tallahassee, Florida   R. H. J.

* C. Frankel, *The Case for Modern Man* (New York: Harper & Brothers, 1956), p. 158.

Contents

It has long been an axiom of mine that the little things are infinitely the most important.

Sherlock Holmes

Introduction

CHEMISTRY is the science that deals with the structure of matter and the transformations it undergoes. This is a very large field of study because the number of different kinds of matter is enormous, and each kind has its own characteristic qualities and attributes. Chemistry tries to answer such questions as these: What is the make-up or composition of this particular kind of matter? Why does it have certain qualities and not others? Will it undergo changes into new, and perhaps more interesting kinds of matter? Can it be produced through the transformation of other, more plentiful kinds of matter?

Above all, the chemist is interested in the "structure" of matter. He believes that each kind of matter, if it could be examined with sufficient magnification, would be found to have a characteristic structure; and that if enough were known about this structure for enough different kinds of matter, all the individual qualities of all kinds of matter could be under-

1

stood. This belief must rely on faith, because the kind of structure that is envisaged is best described as "submicroscopic": it is so fine that even the most powerful of microscopes will not render it visible. Nevertheless, it has been possible to derive a remarkably detailed picture of the structure of matter.

A chemist trying to learn about the structure of matter is not unlike a detective on the scene of a crime. He obtains a clue from this set of observations, and another one from that; then he puts these clues together and builds up a circumstantial case. There is one important difference, however. While the detective's reconstruction of the crime involves real persons who can be questioned, and objects which can be observed, the chemist's picture of the structure of matter can never be verified by direct observation, simply because the structure is too fine to be perceived by the human senses. His case must remain forever circumstantial.

The chemist does the best he can to elucidate the structure of matter within the framework set by these limitations. He tries to make his circumstantial case so air-tight, to arrive at a unified picture of the structure of matter from so many different kinds of evidence, that no one but a confirmed skeptic could entertain any serious doubt about the picture. This is an ambitious goal. Clues must be used wherever they are found. While much of the information concerning the structure of matter comes from the work of chemists on the composition and reactions of individual kinds of matter, an equally important share comes from the work of physicists, whose business it is to discover and study such aspects as are common to *all* matter. Thus, physics includes such studies as the motion of objects under the influence of a force, the behavior of matter after electrification or magnetization, or the flow of heat from one portion of matter to another when there is a difference in temperature.

The two sciences, chemistry and physics, complement one another. The former is concerned with the specific characteristics of individual kinds of matter, and the latter with general properties shared by all matter. It is not uncommon, therefore, to find chemists and physicists working on different aspects of the same general problem.

Submicroscopic Models

No matter how strong the case may be in favor of a certain picture of the structure of matter, it must be remembered that the submicroscopic world and everything in it are still only creations of the human mind. This is necessarily so, for the objects which populate the submicroscopic world are much too small to be sensed directly. Why, then, should chemists bother to consider what would seem to be a purely imaginary realm? After all, isn't chemistry reputed to be an experimental science, standing four-square on direct observation? And aren't there enough mysteries to be solved right here in the macroscopic* world—the world of direct observation—to keep an army of chemists busy for a thousand years? The answer to these questions is that chemists are not satisfied with merely observing nature; they want to understand and explain their observations. To do this the submicroscopic world is indispensable.

Suppose, for example, that we are asked to explain why the pressure exerted by the air in an automobile tire goes up after the automobile is set in motion. The explanation we might offer is that heat is generated as a result of the friction between the moving tire and the road, that the temperature of the air inside the tire consequently goes up, and that this increase in temperature is responsible for the increase in pressure. If this statement were not sufficient, we might add that air is a gas, and that the pressure exerted by air, or by any other gas, has always been found to increase whenever the gas is heated in a container of fixed size. So it should come as no surprise that the pressure in the tire increases also, since this is merely another example of the same well-known phenomenon.

Many people might accept this as a satisfactory explanation. But reflection will show that this kind of explanation raises a new and even larger question: Why does the pressure exerted by *any* gas in a fixed container always go up when the temperature goes up? This is a valid question, and the phenomenon has not been fully explained until an answer can be given.

Since any gas will display the pressure increase, regardless of the material used for the container, it seems logical to suppose that the pressure increase is connected with some feature of the internal structure of gases rather than with some property of the container. In trying to find the answer, one would therefore examine various gases by all sorts of techniques in the hope of perceiving such a structural feature. When this is done, however, no direct perceptual evidence is found.

If the examination has been thorough and imaginative, we may decide that the failure to obtain direct perceptual evidence is not due to lack of skill in observation, but rather to the limitations set by the human senses.

---

* "Macroscopic" comes from the Greek words for "large" and "to view," and hence, literally, applies to visibly large objects.

In other words, the structural features which we have been hoping to observe must be too small to be perceived. When faced with such a conclusion, the physical scientist will usually resort to explanation by means of a submicroscopic "model."

To the physical scientist a "model" is one of two things: it may be a type of picture he draws of the world as it would appear if our senses were like Superman's—unlimited in quality or in range, large or small—or the model may be purely mathematical, and so abstract and general in scope that a pictorialization of it would distort it and limit its scientific usefulness.

The picture models are relatively easy to understand and use, for all of us have been conditioned since childhood to accept as "real" a great many things that we have seen only in the form of pictures or toys. Fortunately, most of chemistry can be explained by means of picture models, and we shall use them often. But now all scientific explanation seems to be tending toward the use and refinement of mathematical models, and it is with these that the advanced student of chemistry must become familiar. A few mathematical models will be mentioned further on, wherever the available picture models seem to be inadequate.

Explanation by Means of Submicroscopic Models

Explanation in terms of submicroscopic models usually involves the following steps:

1. The event or process to be explained is clearly stated, usually in terms of the experimental procedure which led to its observation.
2. Existing models are examined to determine whether or not they can offer an explanation.
3. If existing models are inadequate, a model is *invented* to explain the phenomenon.
4. The invented model is examined for logical consequences that can be confirmed or denied by further experiment.

An example of a "picture model" will help to make this concept clearer. The phenomenon to be explained is this: A gas confined in a container exerts a pressure on the walls of the container. In order to explain this observation, let us propose the following model.

1. The gas consists of a large number of tiny particles.
2. There is enough empty space between the particles so that the particles are free to move.

3. The particles are in constant motion.

Let us see whether this model can account for the observation by picturing in our minds what might be happening. Since there are a great many particles in constant motion, the walls of the container are constantly being bombarded by particles hitting them. Every time such a bombardment occurs, the particle exerts a force or push on the wall while being deflected back into the inside of the container. If the number of such bombardments of the walls by individual particles in unit time were very large, the impression received by a human observer would be that of a steady pressure.

The same model, if made only slightly more elaborate, is capable of explaining why the pressure exerted by a confined gas increases with the temperature. In addition to the three assumptions made above, let us suppose also:

4. The speed at which the particles are moving increases with increasing temperature.

If this assumption were correct, the particles, moving faster at the higher temperature, would collide more often with the walls of the container; and whenever they did collide, they would exert a greater force. Thus, the impression received by an observer would be that of an increased pressure.

A model in which matter is ultimately composed of tiny particles which are in constant motion is quite different from the impression given us by our senses. According to our senses, a gas seems uniform and continuous. Therefore such a model would hardly be taken seriously by many scientists unless it were able to explain also a great many other phenomena. As it turns out, the same basic model, with varying degrees of elaboration, can explain an enormous number of seemingly unrelated phenomena. It can explain such things as why heat flows from a region of higher temperature to one of lower temperature, how chemical reactions take place, or how vitally needed foodstuffs get through the walls surrounding living cells.

Once the basic model has been conceived, its elaboration becomes of first order of importance. Some phenomena can be explained only if the submicroscopic particles envisaged in the basic model have a certain size, or weight, or composition, or shape, or if some of the particles travel at certain speeds, or if they spin, or if they are tiny magnets. As the model becomes more and more elaborate, the number of macroscopic phenomena that can be explained grows larger and larger, until eventually we arrive at a picture of matter that will explain *all* of the behavior of *all* matter. This, of course, is the ultimate goal of the physical sciences.

"Attitude," Not "Method"

The constant switching back and forth between the macroscopic world of observation and the submicroscopic world of theory has been a highly fruitful source of scientific progress. It is indispensable to scientific reasoning. If there were such a thing as a tried-and-true "scientific method," this would have to be part of it.

However, in our opinion there is no such thing as a unique "scientific method." Precisely because scientists are on the frontiers of their fields, they do not know where they are going, and therefore cannot set up sure-fire ways of getting there. What is unique to all good scientists is better described as the "scientific attitude." This attitude combines a burning curiosity with an honest and open mind and a genuine interest in advancing knowledge. The scientist must have the courage to uphold his convictions, and the courage to abandon his theories when they are found wanting.

Groping for knowledge is a highly personal procedure; it takes many forms because each scientist does his research in the manner best suited to his particular temperament. Some, who have a strongly developed scholarly temperament, sort out their ideas and plan their experiments very carefully before they take a single step in the laboratory; others, who are less patient but have an equally clear idea of the problem, prefer to attack it directly in the laboratory. Both methods have their important advantages: the careful planner is more likely to solve his problem without wasteful motion; and the vigorous experimenter is more likely to open up new avenues for further research.

In addition, there are differences in "method" imposed by the nature of the field of study. Chemistry and physics are by and large *experimental* or *laboratory sciences,* whereas astronomy, geology, and meteorology are *field* or *observational sciences.* In the field sciences, one takes nature as it is, observes it in its various aspects, and attempts to understand it. On the other hand, in the laboratory sciences one can ask nature specific questions, and by manipulation and experimentation find answers to these questions.

Research is often most exciting when the results of experiments are totally at variance with what past experience might have led one to expect. The scientist is happiest when his research has created a new problem which demands further research. It is our hope that the reader will discover for himself what the scientific attitude really is.

Chemistry and the Layman

In this book we shall try to describe the current views concerning the structure of matter in such a way as to make them understandable to a person who is not a professional scientist. It is obvious that in a book of this size and intent only a small fraction of the total body of knowledge called chemistry can be studied. We have limited our discussion to the facts and theories relevant to the structure of matter, because such a discussion touches upon most of the fundamental concepts of chemistry. We hope that the reader will thus acquire the kind of background and scientific vocabulary that will enable him, with some additional study, to understand the many scientific issues with which any citizen living in a modern society is faced.

Why should a layman want to understand scientific issues? Perhaps the best answer to this question is that a knowledge of the fundamentals of physics and chemistry has become a necessary adjunct of the educated person. The world in which we live today is complex, rapidly changing, and full of problems that twenty years ago were the concern only of professional scientists. Today these problems demand intelligent decisions made by laymen.

As an illustration, ask yourself the following questions and see whether the correct answers, and actions based upon the answers, are of any consequence to your well-being.

1. What is the source of nuclear energy?
2. What does "radiation" mean?
3. How can new and different life-saving drugs be synthesized?
4. What are the dangers of "fallout"?
5. What are the dangers and remedies of "smog"?
6. Can fresh water be made from sea water?
7. Can we harness the sun's energy?

The answers to these and hundreds of similar questions are no longer the sole concern of the experts. They represent issues you may be asked to vote on, to approve, or to appropriate money for. Persuasive voices, using all the psychological means at their disposal, will try to move you to action or create apathy. The kind of citizens our society needs will have to have more than sales resistance to pressure groups. They will need positive information bearing on such questions as these.

Suggestions for Further Reading

L. Pauling, "Chemistry," *Scientific American,* Sept. 1950, p. 32.

J. R. Oppenheimer, "The Age of Science: 1900–1950," *Scientific American,* Sept. 1950, p. 20.

Ann Roe, "A Psychologist Examines 64 Scientists," *Scientific American,* Nov. 1952, p. 21.

W. Weaver, "Fundamental Questions in Science," *Scientific American,* Sept. 1953, p. 47.

Bernard and Judith Mausner, "The Anti-Scientific Attitude," *Scientific American,* Feb. 1955, p. 35.

L. M. Terman, "Are Scientists Different?" *Scientific American,* Jan. 1955, p. 25.

F. P. Armitage, *History of Chemistry* (London: Longmans, Green & Co., Inc., 1920).

J. C. Brown, *History of Chemistry* (London: J. & A. Churchill, 1920).

F. Ferchl and A. Süssenguth, *A Pictorial History of Chemistry* (London: Wm. Heinemann, Ltd., 1939).

Henry M. Smith, *Torchbearers of Chemistry* (New York: Academic Press, 1949).

W. A. Tilden, *Famous Chemists* (New York: E. P. Dutton & Co., Inc., 1921).

E. Farber, *The Evolution of Chemistry* (New York: Ronald Press Co., 1952).

C. H. Waddington, *The Scientific Attitude,* rev. ed. (Baltimore: Penguin Books, Inc., 1948).

G. Holton and D. H. D. Roller, *Foundations of Modern Physical Science* (Reading, Mass.: Addison-Wesley Publishing Co., Inc., 1958).

K. Hutton, *Chemistry* (Baltimore: Penguin Books, Inc., 1957).

A. Einstein, *Essays in Science* (New York: Philosophical Library, 1934).

Suggestions for Supplementary Textbooks

S. M. Brooks, *Basic Facts of General Chemistry* (Philadelphia: W. B. Saunders Company, 1956).

P. R. Frey, *College Chemistry* (Englewood Cliffs, N. J.: Prentice-Hall, Inc., 1958).

W. N. Jones, Jr., *General Chemistry* (New York: Blakiston Company, 1954).

James Kendall, *At Home Among the Atoms* (New York: The Century Co., 1929).

L. Pauling, *College Chemistry* (San Francisco: W. H. Freeman & Company, 1950).

J. H. Hildebrand and R. E. Powell, *Principles of Chemistry* (New York: Macmillan Company, 1952).

J. V. Quagliano, *Chemistry* (Englewood Cliffs, N. J.: Prentice-Hall, Inc., 1958).

J. I. Routh, *20th Century Chemistry* (Philadelphia: W. B. Saunders Company, 1958).

H. J. Sienko and R. A. Plane, *Chemistry* (New York: McGraw-Hill Book Company, Inc., 1957).

N. D. Cheronis, J. B. Parsons, and C. E. Ronneberg, *The Study of the Physical World* (New York: Houghton Mifflin Company, 1950).

E. J. Cable, R. W. Getchell, and W. H. Kadesch, *The Physical Sciences* (Englewood Cliffs, N. J.: Prentice-Hall, Inc., 1951).

G. Gamow, *Matter, Earth and Sky* (Englewood Cliffs, N. J.: Prentice-Hall, Inc., 1958).

K. Krauskopf, *Fundamentals of Physical Science,* 4th ed. (New York: McGraw-Hill Book Company, Inc., 1959).

J. J. G. McCue, *The World of Atoms* (New York: Ronald Press Co., 1956).

The best and safest method of philosophising we should say seems to be, first to inquire diligently into the properties of things, and of establishing these properties by experiment, and then to proceed more slowly to hypotheses for the explanation of them.

Isaac Newton (1642–1727)

2 *Mixtures and Pure Substances*

THE MATTER we encounter every day is almost always a complex mixture. The things that are most familiar to us—and which we might expect to be easy to classify and study—are of such complexity as to make the analytical chemist shudder. The air we breathe is a mixture of at least five substances; gasoline is a complex mixture of more than a dozen substances; Portland cement consists of five or more substances; steel, though consisting largely of iron, owes its properties to the admixture of a number of other substances during its manufacture. Virtually all living or once-living forms of matter are complicated almost beyond description; it would be a hopeless job to count all the different substances present in the human body.

There are few cases where the matter that we encounter in ordinary experience is "pure," that is, consists of only a single substance. Distilled water is a pure substance; so is the copper that we use in electrical wiring, and the granulated sugar that we add to our coffee. But one is hard-put to extend this list much further. Even such a pure-looking substance as ordinary table salt consists not only of sodium chloride crystals, but also of small amounts of additives in order to delay clumping.

Because of the great complexity of ordinary matter, chemistry as a science had rather a slow start. It was only after the necessity for studying the behavior of "unmixed" substances had been recognized, and methods for separating the mixtures in ordinary use into their components had been perfected, that the development of chemistry became rapid. The wonderfully simple and straightforward laws of chemical combination and composition could be discovered only after chemists began to deal with pure materials.

This procedure—the separation of complex mixtures into their components which are then studied individually—illustrates a general strategy of the laboratory sciences. Complex, seemingly insoluble problems can often be solved by breaking them down into a number of smaller problems, each amenable to solution.

Physical Properties of Matter

The concept of a pure substance is so important that it deserves careful consideration. Many of the materials that we encounter in ordinary life are obviously not pure substances, but rather complex mixtures. For example, a T-bone steak consists of bone matter, meat, and fat. Wood consists of distinct regions of characteristically different appearance which are responsible for its grain. In both examples we know just from their appearance that we are dealing with mixtures of substances. Matter with these characteristics is referred to as *heterogeneous.**

There are, however, a good many materials which are perfectly uniform throughout; that is, any one portion is just like every other portion. In many cases, these materials consist of more than one substance. Examples that have been mentioned are air, gasoline, and steel. Materials that are uniform throughout are referred to as *homogeneous.*† When a homogeneous material consists of more than one substance, it is called a *solution.* From the examples that have been given, it is clear that a solution may be gaseous, liquid, or solid.

* A term derived from a Greek root meaning "of other kinds."
† A term derived from a Greek root meaning "of the same kind or nature."

A difficult problem facing the chemist is to distinguish between solutions and pure substances, since both are perfectly uniform even upon microscopic examination. He solves the problem by subjecting the homogeneous sample to one or several of the procedures that are capable of separating mixtures into their pure components. If these operations lead to the separation of the sample into a number of substances with different properties, then he reasons that the original sample must have been a solution. On the other hand, if the properties of the sample remain unchanged, then he is reasonably sure that he is dealing with a pure substance.

What are these properties which may or may not be changing? The most obvious ones are those that can be noted with our unaided senses, such as the color of the material, or its odor, or perhaps even its taste. During the nineteenth century it was not uncommon for a chemist to sample the taste of something he had just prepared—without swallowing it, of course. But the unaided senses are not sensitive enough to detect small differences in properties, and it is usually more conclusive to examine other properties that can be measured more exactly with scientific instruments. Some of these properties are listed and defined below.

1. *The density* is the weight per unit volume. The density is usually expressed in grams per cubic centimeter (g/cc).
2. *The melting point* (m.p.) of a solid is the temperature at which the solid is converted to a liquid.
3. *The boiling point* (b.p.) of a liquid is the temperature at which the liquid is rapidly converted into vapor, the conversion being accompanied by the formation of bubbles. The boiling point varies with the prevailing pressure, but is normally reported at a pressure of one atmosphere (atm).
4. *The refractive index* is related to the speed at which light travels in the given sample of matter. It turns out that this rather unusual property can be measured easily and accurately in terms of the angles at which the light enters and leaves the substance.
5. *The conductivity for electricity* is a measure of the ease with which an electric current can pass through the substance. Copper is an excellent conductor, but glass is a poor conductor or good insulator.
6. *The viscosity* of a liquid or gas is a measure of the ease with which the liquid or gas will flow. For example, water will flow much more readily than motor oil.
7. *The crystalline form of a solid* is the characteristic shape in which the solid separates from liquid solutions or a melt. Pure solids usually separate in the form of crystals, that is, in the form of solid bodies which are bounded by symmetrically arranged plane surfaces.

8. *The hardness* of a solid is a measure of how easily the surface of the solid may be scratched.

The density, refractive index, conductivity for electricity, viscosity, and hardness all vary with the temperature, and must therefore be measured after the sample has been brought to some definite temperature, often chosen to be 25°C (77°F).

The Operational Definition of a Pure Substance

Let us suppose that we want a sample of really pure water. In most communities, the tap water is "pure" only in the medical sense; that is, it is free from harmful or poisonous ingredients. The tap water is not "pure" in the chemical sense since it usually contains small amounts of dissolved minerals and gases, which we shall call "impurities." To the chemist, water is pure only if it contains no impurities whatsoever.

Our job then is to obtain chemically pure water from the tap water. There are a number of procedures that one might use, some of which will be described later in this chapter. A convenient method is to cool the water and to allow about half of it to freeze. The impurities tend to remain in the liquid, and the solid ice that freezes out is likely to be quite pure. The ice may then be separated from the liquid, placed in a separate container, and allowed to melt. This process may be repeated as often as necessary.

Another method of purification, which we shall discuss later, is distillation. The distilled water is more nearly pure than the original undistilled sample.

After each purification step, the purified sample of water is examined and several of its physical properties are determined. There will probably be a definite difference between the properties of the tap water and those of the water sample obtained in the first purification step, indicating that some impurities have been removed. As the purified water is subjected to further purification, the differences in the properties of the doubly, triply, and so on, purified water become progressively smaller, and soon a sample is obtained the properties of which are not changed on further purification. Such a sample is then accepted as "pure."

Some of the properties of pure water are as follows: pure water boils at 100°C (at one atmosphere pressure); it has a refractive index of 1.333 and a density of 0.997 g/cc at 25°C; pure ice melts at 0°C. These are the properties of *all* samples of pure water, regardless of their origin, the nature of the impurities they contained before purification, and the location of the laboratory where the purification took place. Hence, we conclude that these properties are characteristic of the substance, water. If in the future we en-counter another liquid with boiling point 100°C, density 0.997, refractive index 1.333, and which is identical in all other observable respects with an authentic sample of pure water, then we assert that this liquid must also consist of pure water.

Reflection will show that the method of recognizing a pure substance by its properties is exactly the method we use to recognize objects or persons in everyday life. Thus, we recognize a friend by the shape of his head, the color of his hair, or the tone of his voice, and in a similar man-ner we recognize a pure substance by its boiling point, density, or other properties. There is one important difference, however. While the friend may alter his appearance at will, the physical properties of a pure substance under a given set of conditions are characteristic of the material and are inseparable from it. If Charlie gets a suntan and grows a beard he is still Charlie, but if a liquid boils at 80°C it can no longer be assumed to be water.

In short, a given substance is simply the sum of its properties, and can thus be recognized by these properties under any circumstances. When you ask "What is iron?" the best answer is that iron is a substance that melts at 1535°C, boils at 3000°C and one atmosphere pressure, has a density of 7.86 at 20°C, reacts with oxygen, and so on. Since the complete set of prop-erties is unique for any given pure substance, it is obvious that if two samples of matter have identical sets of properties they are samples of the same pure substance.

It will be noted that we have defined the term "pure substance" entirely by means of *experimental operations.* Such a definition is called an "opera-tional definition." The definition is based on the experimental fact that when an impure substance is subjected to successive purification proce-dures, the properties soon reach a definite constant limit, at which time the substance is accepted as pure.

There is an alternative nonoperational definition of a pure substance which is based on the theory that matter is ultimately composed of sub-microscopic particles, called "molecules." In terms of this theory, a pure substance is simply a sample of matter in which all the molecules are exactly alike.

The States of Matter

An obvious classification of matter is on the basis of its "state," which may be solid, liquid, or gaseous. Water can exist in all three states: as ice, as liquid water, and as steam. Water is one of the few substances with which the average person is familiar in all three of its states. The reason is simple: the temperature range over which transitions among the various states take place is quite narrow—100° on the centigrade scale—and the melting point and boiling point are not too far from room temperature.

Most other common substances are familiar to us in only one state, either because the range of temperature required for conversion from one state to another is wider than that for water, or because the transition temperatures are far from room temperature. An example is the substance iron, familiar only as a solid. However, at a temperature of 1535°C iron becomes liquid, and at 3000°C and one atmosphere pressure it is converted to a gas (a vapor). On the other hand, oxygen is best known as a gas. However, at a temperature of −183°C and one atmosphere pressure it becomes a liquid, and with further cooling it solidifies at −218.4°C.

The three states of matter can be operationally defined in terms of their macroscopic characteristics (we will defer until later a consideration of how they are defined theoretically in terms of submicroscopic particles), as follows:

The *solid state* is characterized by (1) high density, usually in the range from 1 to 10 grams per cubic centimeter; (2) rigid shape; (3) slight compressibility; (4) only slight expansion at atmospheric pressure as the temperature is raised—usually less than 0.01% per degree centigrade.

The *liquid state* is characterized by (1) high density, but usually somewhat less than that of the corresponding solid; (2) lack of definite shape (liquids conform to the shape of the containing vessel); (3) slight compressibility, but usually somewhat greater than that of the corresponding solid; (4) only slight expansion at atmospheric pressure as the temperature is raised—usually about 0.1% per degree centigrade.

The *gaseous state* is characterized by (1) low density; (2) indefinite shape and volume (gases fill completely any container into which they are placed); (3) high compressibility; (4) considerable expansion—about 0.3% per degree centigrade—when heated at constant pressure.

Isolation and Purification of Substances

Since the world is made up largely of mixtures of varying complexity, and since chemical reactions become intelligible only when we deal with pure substances, it is of the utmost importance to have reliable methods by which mixtures can be separated into their constituent substances.

If the mixture is not homogeneous, then it is sometimes possible to separate the various homogeneous components by mechanical means. For example, gold is separated in this way from the accompanying gravel. Usually such mechanical means are not very successful, however, and other techniques must be used.

In the following pages, we shall discuss several of the techniques that have been developed for the separation of mixtures and the isolation of the pure components. We shall describe each technique as it is used in the laboratory with fairly small samples, but the reader should realize that these operations are also carried out commercially with carload quantities of materials in the chemical industry, using large-scale modifications of the equipment.

1. Distillation

Distillation depends on the fact that the components of a liquid solution* usually differ in their volatility,† that is, in the ease with which they can be vaporized. When a solution is heated to boiling, the vapor which boils away contains a higher concentration of the more volatile component than the original liquid. If this vapor is now collected separately and condensed back to the liquid state, the new liquid condensate obviously will be richer in the more volatile component. The process of boiling followed by condensation may be repeated many times, until eventually the condensate is so highly enriched in the more volatile of the two components that it may be regarded as a pure sample of the more volatile component.

In order to see how purification by distillation works, let us consider a liquid solution containing equal weights of water and of acetone. Acetone is an organic liquid which is often used in chemical operations, especially as a solvent for other substances. As we know, water boils at 100°C. Acetone is more volatile than water, and pure acetone boils at 56°C. The 50–50 mixture initially boils at an intermediate temperature, which has been measured and found to be 66°C. This boiling point gradually rises, as the more volatile acetone vaporizes, until it reaches that of pure water.

The vapor obtained from the 50–50 mixture contains 92% of acetone—an enormous enrichment. If this vapor is condensed, the resultant liquid of course has the same composition, namely, 92% acetone. If this liquid is

---

* See page 11 for a working definition of "solution."

† *Volatile* is from the Latin "to fly"; as an English word it also means "giddy, lighthearted."

boiled and the vapor condensed, the new liquid contains 97% acetone; in other words, it is almost pure acetone. The process may be repeated as often as necessary until acetone of any desired degree of purity is obtained.

The apparatus for carrying out a simple distillation is shown in Figure 2-1. The liquid is brought to a gentle boil in the boiling flask *A*, and the vapor rises into the condenser tube *B*, the walls of which are cooled, normally with tap water. Since the temperature of the condenser is below the boiling point, the vapor condenses to a liquid and is collected in the receiving flask, *C*. Since the vapor is always richer in the more volatile component, the liquid remaining in the boiling flask becomes gradually richer in the less volatile component as more of the more volatile component boils away. Eventually, when virtually all of the more volatile component has been distilled, the liquid remaining is a nearly pure sample of the less volatile component. The solution has thus been separated into its pure components.

Devices are available in which the process of boiling-followed-by-con-

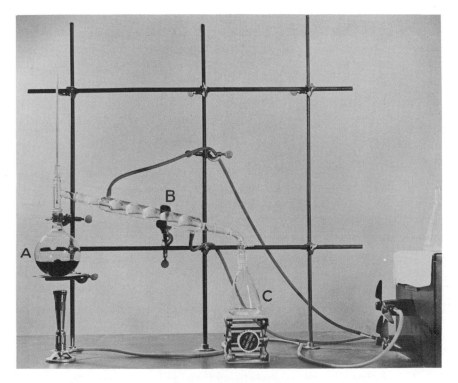

Fig. 2-1. A simple distillation.

densation is carried out time after time in a single apparatus. One such apparatus is shown in Figure 2-2. It differs from the simple apparatus of Figure 2-1 by the inclusion of a so-called fractionating column, D in which this repetitive process occurs.

2. Recrystallization

Recrystallization is an excellent method for the purification of slightly impure solid substances. The method depends on the fact that the solubility of most solid substances in a given liquid increases markedly with

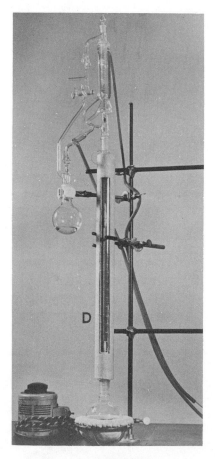

Fig. 2-2. Apparatus for fractional distillation. Condensation and boiling takes place repeatedly on the large surface area of the fractionating column which is packed with glass rings.

Fig. 2-3. Steps in Recrystallization.

increasing temperature. The slightly impure solid is dissolved in a suitable quantity of a liquid—perhaps water or alcohol—which is kept at or just below its boiling temperature. When most or all of the solid has been dissolved, the hot solution is filtered; that is, the solution is allowed to drip through a filter paper or a porous glass disk which permits the liquid to pass but retains specks of dust or other solid impurities. The hot filtered solution is then set aside to cool. As the temperature drops, the solubility of the solid decreases, and the solid starts to crystallize, leaving the impurities dissolved in the solution. The solid crystals are then separated from the remaining liquid by filtration. The purity of the crystals is usually measured by the sharpness of their melting point, that is, by the narrowness of the temperature range over which melting occurs. If a substance is perfectly pure, all of it will melt at the same temperature.

Some laboratory apparatus used in recrystallization is shown in Figure 2-3.

3. Solvent extraction

Solvent extraction is often employed in order to separate a single substance from a liquid solution containing several substances. The method works as follows: the original solution is placed into a *separatory funnel* (shown in Figure 2-4), and a second liquid, which we shall call the *extracting solvent,* is added. The extracting solvent must possess two important characteristics: it must be insoluble in the initial solution, and the substance to be extracted must be more soluble in the extracting solvent than in the initial solution.

For example, let us suppose that we wish to separate iodine from a solution containing water, iodine, and sugar. We place the solution into a separatory funnel and add a roughly equal volume of the liquid *carbon tetrachloride,* which possesses the correct characteristics of an extracting solvent for iodine. Carbon tetrachloride does not dissolve in water, and neither water nor sugar is soluble in carbon tetrachloride. But iodine is a hundred times as soluble in carbon tetrachloride as in water; that is, if the separatory funnel is shaken so that the two liquids are brought into close contact, a hundred parts of iodine will pass into the carbon tetrachloride for every one part remaining with the sugar in the water solution. The carbon tetrachloride, which is more dense than water, is then drawn off

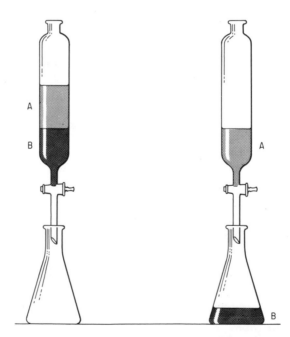

Fig. 2-4. Separation of two immiscible solutions A and B by means of the separatory funnel. The denser of the two liquids (B) is drained off through the stopcock.

through the stopcock at the bottom of the separatory funnel, leaving behind the sugar and water. When the carbon tetrachloride is evaporated, the solid residue is quite pure iodine.

4. Chromatography

Chromatography makes use of the fact that the surfaces of solids are able to attract other substances and hold them more or less tightly. This process is known as *adsorption.** For ordinary solids the amount of other substances that can be adsorbed in this way is rather small, but when the solid is given a large surface area by being ground to a very fine particle size, it can adsorb appreciable amounts. The tenacity with which different substances are held by a given adsorbing surface can vary widely, and when it does vary, the substances can be separated. The method works as follows:

Let us suppose that we wish to separate a mixture of two substances that differ greatly in the firmness with which they are adsorbed by a given solid. After the mixture has been adsorbed, the surface carrying the two substances is washed with a liquid that is capable of dissolving both substances but not the adsorbing surface. The substance which is held less firmly washes off relatively easily, and may therefore be separated from the other substance which comes off only with difficulty. In the laboratory, this operation is carried out most easily by packing a straight glass tube with the adsorbing solid. The mixture of two or more substances to be separated is introduced at the top, and then is gradually moved down the column by repeated addition of a suitable liquid. This liquid carries each component of the mixture down the column at a rate that depends on how firmly the component is adsorbed. Those components that are adsorbed most firmly move most slowly. The differences in the rates of movement result in the separation of the mixture into distinct bands, each representing one component of the mixture, as is shown in Figure 2-5.

Appropriate modifications of chromatography are used to separate mixtures of solids, liquids, or of gases. In the latter case, the "carrier" fluid is, of course, a gas. The advantage of chromatography is that one can separate very small amounts of complex mixtures with little likelihood of the process leading to the destruction of any of the substances in the mixture. The disadvantage is that the substances are collected in the presence of a large amount of carrier fluid from which they are not always easy to

---

* From the Latin "to suck from."

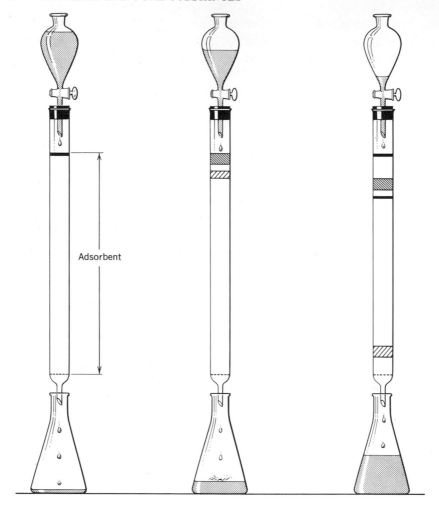

Adsorbent

Fig. 2-5. Separation by chromatography.

separate. Originally the method was used for mixtures of colored substances whose passage down the tube could be followed visually,* but
methods are now available for applying the method to colorless substances.

*   *   *

By means of these processes and others, the complex mixtures ordinarily
encountered in nature can be separated. Since the fundamental nature of

* Hence the name "chromatography," from a Greek word meaning "color writing."

matter is revealed most clearly from the behavior of *pure* substances, the methods of separation are of enormous importance. Without the ready availability of such pure substances the development of modern chemistry would have been impossible.

Suggestions for Further Reading

W. H. Stein and S. Moore, "Chromatography," *Scientific American,* March 1951, p. 35.

R. L. Fullman, "The Growth of Crystals," *Scientific American,* March 1955, p. 74.

A. J. Birch, *How Chemistry Works* (London: Sigma Books, Ltd., 1949) chap. 3.

L. Pauling, *College Chemistry* (San Francisco: W. H. Freeman & Company, 1950) chap. 2.

3 *Chemical Change,*
The Source of New Substances

The Macroscopic Characteristics of Chemical Change

Change is the rule rather than the exception in the observable world. In this chapter we want to focus attention on one class of change—chemical change—and to become familiar with its macroscopic characteristics. In order to obtain a clear picture of what we mean by "chemical change" let us consider a few examples of substances undergoing it.

The rusting of iron is a familiar transformation. The strong, ductile metal is slowly transformed into a brittle, easily crumbled red powder of little mechanical strength. This red powder is a new substance in no way

24

like the parent metal. For example, the magnetic property commonly associated with iron no longer exists in this new material. The process of combustion in which coal, wood, or oil is consumed is another dramatic chemical change. The products of combustion of wood in no way resemble the original wood, these being largely a gas (carbon dioxide), water, and ash. The conversion of the food we eat to living tissue, the growth of plants, the souring of milk, the decay of vegetation are all examples of chemical changes being carried on by living organisms.

The cooking of an egg, the conversion of high-boiling crude oils into gasoline, the production of metallic aluminum from the stony-looking mineral bauxite, the hardening of mortar, the evolution of gas that occurs when baking powder is moistened, these are all examples of chemical changes in which one substance disappears and one or more new substances, with completely new sets of physical and chemical properties, appear in its place.

All these, of course, represent only a very few of the literally millions of chemical changes known to chemists. But all chemical changes, both those familiar to the layman and occurring daily, and those carried out only with difficulty in the laboratory, have a number of attributes in common. We must become familiar with these attributes before we can formulate an acceptable theory to explain chemical change.

The characteristics which *all* chemical changes (also called "chemical reactions") have in common are:

1. The substances that are present initially (the *reactants*) disappear.
2. One or several new substances (the *products*) appear as the reaction proceeds and the reactants disappear.
3. The properties of the products are recognizably different from those of the reactants.
4. Energy in the form of heat, light, or electricity is released or absorbed* in the course of the chemical change.

Although chemists today have observed and verified these characteristics many, many times, the correct description of chemical change is a relatively recent accomplishment. As recently as 1800, combustion, one of the commonest of chemical changes, was thought to involve the evolution of a mysterious nonmaterial substance called phlogiston.† The modern view of chemical change had its beginnings with the researches of the

---

* Literally, absorb means "to suck away," i.e., to cause to disappear. A substance *ab*sorbed by another disappears into it, is mingled with it, whereas, as noted earlier, a substance *ad*sorbs another onto its surface.

† An archaic scientific term derived from a Greek word meaning "inflammable."

French chemist, Antoine Lavoisier, in the latter half of the eighteenth century. Lavoisier demonstrated that the process of combustion does not involve the mysterious phlogiston, but that it has the typical characteristics of a chemical reaction.

The Elements

Man has always desired to make the complex simple. The earliest writings and legends reveal a preoccupation with a uniform, underlying "reality." Thus, the Greek philosopher, Empedocles, proclaimed in the 5th century B.C. that the universe is composed of a multitude of combinations of the four "elements": *earth, air, fire, and water.*

A century earlier, another Greek, Thales, had proposed the theory that there is only one element, water, and that the multiplicity of the universe consists simply of variations of this one substance. In the years that followed, various other substances were championed as being the ultimate building blocks of the universe, but none was universally accepted. All of the various "elements" that were espoused suffered one serious shortcoming—their selection was based on supposition rather than experiment, and no experiments were seriously undertaken to test the validity of each theory.

It was not until 1661 that the Englishman, Robert Boyle, in his book *The Sceptical Chymist,* proposed a definition of an "element" that has

Robert Boyle: 1627–1691

Boyle may be called the founder of modern chemistry. He recognized the intrinsic value of chemistry, in addition to its role as an adjunct to medicine. He introduced rigorous experimental methods and rebelled against the obscurantism of the alchemists. He was the first to distinguish between mixtures and compounds, and his definition of an element is still valid today.

withstood the test of time and experiment and, with slight modification, is still in use today. In Boyle's own words: "And to prevent mistakes, I must advertize You, that I now mean by Elements, . . . certain Primitive and Simple, or perfectly unmingled bodies; which not being made of any other bodies, or of one another, are the Ingredients of which all those call'd perfectly mixt Bodies are immediately compounded, and into which they are ultimately resolved."

In modern language Boyle is saying that there are certain substances (Boyle specifies no number) that can be thought of as being of ultimate simplicity, that is, they cannot be broken down into yet simpler substances; and it is these that, in various combinations, make up all of the complex substances ("mixt Bodies") of the universe. Note that Boyle gives us a test, or experiment, the results of which can be used to determine whether or not a given substance is an "element": *if the substance cannot be broken down into yet simpler substances by any means known to the chemist, it must be classified as an element.* The reader will note that Boyle's definition is an *operational* definition since a substance is classified as an element solely on the basis of experimental operations.

Thus, an element is any substance that will resist all known methods of decomposition. But in a growing science, there is always the possibility that new methods will be discovered which can break down some of the substances that had previously been thought of as elements. This has actually happened a number of times. For example, the substance potash was for a long time thought to be an element. However in 1807, by passing an electric current through moist potash, Sir Humphrey Davy demonstrated that potash is really a "mixt Body" consisting of familiar elements and of a new metallic substance which he called "potassium." The question remains whether, with potassium, we have at last arrived at an element, or whether potassium is yet another complex substance which is even more difficult to break down than the potash from which it was obtained. In the light of Boyle's definition, this question is answered by saying that all efforts at further decomposition have been resisted, and that potassium therefore meets all requirements and must be accepted as an element. Thus, according to Boyle's definition, we can never be sure that our list of the elements is final and complete.

Since Boyle's time, fortunately, independent theories have been developed, of which more will be said later, which give us criteria for making unequivocal statements about whether a given substance is an element or not. On this basis there are known today 88 naturally occurring elements and 14 synthetic ones.* (See inside front cover for a list of the elements.)

According to Boyle's definition, an element must be a fairly stable substance. It must be at least stable enough to enable one to isolate it in the pure state, determine its properties, and see whether or not it can be broken down into yet simpler substances. Therefore, the list of the elements was not revised when it was discovered during the last few decades that, under the influence of intense heat or high voltage, the stable elements of the chemist can be broken down into simpler but highly unstable components. Some of these experiments will be described in Chapter 8.

Compounds and Mixtures

Let us now consider Boyle's "mixt Bodies" or *compounds,* as we shall call them.

A compound is a substance composed of two or more elements in a definite proportion by weight.

But a compound is *not* merely a mixture of the elements, for the original properties of the elements have been lost and replaced by an entirely new set of properties which are characteristic of the compound. In reacting to form the compound, the elements have entered into a state of firm chemical combination; they are held together in the compound by chemical bonds which are so strong that the compound remains intact even when it is subjected to purification procedures, such as distillation or chromatography. Thus, compounds are pure substances, and we see that there are really two classes of pure substances—elements and compounds.

For example, water is a compound consisting of 11.2% by weight of hydrogen and 88.8% by weight of oxygen, in chemical combination. That is, hydrogen has reacted with oxygen to produce the new substance, water.

Carbon dioxide (Dry Ice) is a compound consisting of 27.3% by weight of carbon and 72.7% by weight of oxygen, in chemical combination. Sodium chloride is a compound consisting of 39.3% sodium and 60.7% chlorine, in chemical combination. Sulfuric acid is a compound consisting of 32.70% sulfur, 65.26% oxygen, and 2.04% hydrogen, in chemical combination.

In each of these examples it must be emphasized that if the percentages

---

* *Synthetic* is used here as a chemical term describing what is prepared artificially in the laboratory, as opposed to what occurs in nature. It is derived from a Greek word meaning "placed together."

of the elements were significantly different, we would not have the compound in question. That is, if the percentages of the elements were different, the physical as well as the chemical properties would be different. By "chemical properties" we mean the types of reactions that the substance will undergo, and the readiness with which these reactions will take place.

The fact that the composition of a compound has a definite and fixed value gives us a criterion for distinguishing between compounds and mixtures. The percentage composition of a mixture is *not fixed* but can be varied arbitrarily. Thus the label on pancake syrup may state that it contains 15% maple syrup and 85% cane syrup, which might suggest that it is a compound of the corresponding elements. But the next brand we pick up could very well contain 20% maple and 80% cane syrup, and a third might contain 50% of each. In other words, we can vary the percentage composition in any way we like and still have a product that is correctly labeled pancake syrup.

The possibility for such arbitrary variation does not exist in the case of a pure compound. Sodium chloride always consists of 39.3% sodium and 60.7% chlorine, and any effort to produce sodium chloride of a different composition would be futile. If one takes exactly 60.7 g of gaseous chlorine and 39.3 g of metallic sodium and allows them to combine, one obtains 100.0 g of the compound sodium chloride. Neither chlorine nor sodium is in excess, and all of each constituent is used up in the formation of the compound. Thus, if the constituent elements are allowed to react in the same ratio as they have in the final compound, there will be no uncombined elements left over. On the other hand, if instead of 39.3 g of sodium one uses 41.3 g, while still using the same amount of chlorine, chemical combination will occur just as before, and one will again obtain 100.0 g of sodium chloride, but 2.0 g of sodium will be left uncombined. The 2.0 g corresponds exactly to the difference between the amount demanded by the ratio of sodium to chlorine in the compound and the amounts actually used. The behavior would be analogous if excess chlorine were used, except that in this case unreacted chlorine would be found at the conclusion of the experiment.*

Behavior of this type is observed in all chemical reactions in which the elements unite to form only one compound. When more than one compound is formed, the situation is naturally more complicated, but the

---

* It is not possible here to have an excess of *both* elements. Thus, if we take 41.3 g of sodium and 62.7 g of chlorine (a 2 g "excess" of each), we find that the 2 g "excess" of chlorine reacts with the "excess" of sodium in the ratio required by the composition of the compound, leaving 0.7 g of unreacted sodium.

composition of each of the compounds is still fixed and definite. Further discussion will be reserved for Chapter 4.

The Formation of Solutions

In most cases when a solution is formed, the substances involved in forming the solution are not permanently altered but can be recovered unchanged. An example is the dissolving of sugar in water. Evaporation of the water results in the recovery of unchanged sugar.

Sometimes, however, the formation of the solution is accompanied by a chemical reaction. When this happens, the constituents are profoundly altered and are not recoverable in their original form. For example, when a metal is dissolved in an acid, hydrogen gas is liberated and heat is evolved. Evaporation of the solution leads to the recovery of a compound of the metal rather than to recovery of the original metal.

Intermediate cases exist in which the original substances can be recovered unchanged, but where one may deduce from the fact that heat is liberated or absorbed when the solution is being formed, that some chemical interaction is taking place. Sulfuric acid in water is a solution of this type.

Physical Change Contrasted with Chemical Change

You may wonder how a given change is known to be a chemical change in the sense already discussed, rather than a physical change. In a physical change, a substance is heated, or cooled, or compressed, or otherwise exposed to some new external condition without, however, losing its chemical identity. When the original external conditions are restored, the substance regains its original physical properties. Water is still the same chemical substance, "water," whether in the liquid, solid, or gaseous state; the main difference is the temperature at which these states are stable. On the other hand, in a chemical change the initial substance disappears and new substances with entirely different physical and chemical properties appear in its place.

Methods of Bringing about Chemical Change

How can one *cause* a chemical reaction to occur? Frequently the simple act of bringing two substances together will result in their reacting with one another. Thus, if gaseous chlorine is brought into contact with metallic potassium, potassium chloride, with none of the properties of the two reactants, is rapidly formed with the evolution of considerable energy. Or if nitric oxide (a compound of nitrogen and oxygen) comes in contact with oxygen, a spontaneous reaction occurs and the new compound, nitrogen dioxide, is formed. On the other hand, the mixing of two substances will frequently not result in a chemical reaction until some stimulus is supplied. For example, zinc powder and sulfur when mixed together in the dry state do not undergo a reaction. However, if a lighted match is touched to the mixture, a violent reaction ensues with the formation of the compound, zinc sulfide.

Single substances can also undergo chemical reactions. A common example is *decomposition,* in which a compound breaks down into simpler substances. Thus, when mercuric oxide (a compound of mercury and oxygen) is heated strongly, it decomposes into metallic mercury and gaseous oxygen. Another well-known type of reaction which involves only a single substance is one in which the original substance disappears and a single new substance appears in its place. An example is the historic experiment performed by the German chemist, F. Wöhler, in 1828. Wöhler heated a sample of ammonium cyanate (a compound containing carbon, oxygen, nitrogen, and hydrogen), and thereby converted it into urea, which is an entirely different compound but has exactly the same composition as the starting material. Since urea is a

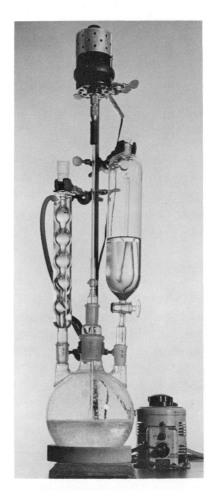

Fig. 3-1. Typical apparatus for carrying out a chemical reaction. One of the reactants is in the large flask, and a second reactant is added from the dropping funnel while the mixture is stirred.

product of *human metabolism,* this experiment helped discredit the widely held belief that a mysterious "vital force" was necessary for the formation of compounds found in living organisms; thus, it partially cleared the way for modern organic chemistry. The experiment suggests something interesting for further consideration, namely that the nature and properties of a compound must depend on more than merely the kind and amounts of the elements that go to make it up. And indeed, we shall see in Chapter 14 that the nature of a compound depends also on the way in which the elements are combined.

Light is capable of stimulating chemical changes. In plants, the production of organic compounds from air, carbon dioxide, and water is an all-important reaction which requires light. And in photography, the light entering the camera sets off the chemical reaction which ultimately leads to the production of an image on the photographic film.

Electricity is yet another stimulus for chemical change. For example, the passage of an electric current through water results in its decomposition to the constituent elements—hydrogen and oxygen.

Why these various agents are effective, and why some reactions occur spontaneously while others do not, can be explained theoretically, but not until we have an understanding of the submicroscopic models for elements and compounds. Meanwhile our discussion continues its rough parallel of the history of chemistry. Having grasped the concept of material substances as composed ultimately of simple elements, which combine in certain regular ways under stated conditions, we will find in the next chapter that some of the most important laws of chemical combination involve the weights of the combining substances. Since weight is a quality that can be operationally defined, we find ourselves still in the macroscopic world of the chemical laboratory. In the latter part of Chapter 4 we move into the world beyond the reach of the laboratory apparatus—the submicroscopic world set forth in the atomic theory of John Dalton—to explain the chemical behavior of the macroscopic world.

Suggestions for Further Reading

Mary Elvira Weeks, *The Discovery of the Elements* 6th ed. (Easton, Pa.: *Journal of Chemical Education,* 1956).

Robert Boyle, *The Skeptical Chymist* (New York: E. P. Dutton & Co., Inc., 1911).

James Kendall, *At Home Among the Atoms* (New York: The Century Co., 1929).

L. T. More, *The Life and Works of the Hon. Robert Boyle* (London: Oxford University Press, 1944).

W. Tilden, *Famous Chemists* (New York: E. P. Dutton & Co., Inc., 1921) chaps. 1, 7.

The Laws of

Chemical Change

The Measurement of Weight

The weight of a substance can be measured accurately by means of an analytical balance such as the one shown in Figure. 4-1. The balance makes use of the lever principle. There is a central support which is constructed so that the beam can move with a minimum of friction, and the two lever arms are of equal length. A pointer is fixed to the center of the beam and extends nearly to the base of the upright. A pan is attached on each side. The unknown weight is placed on one pan, and known weights are placed on the other. When the weights on the two pans are equal, the beam is level, as indicated by the pointer. Since the weight on one pan is known, the unknown weight on the other pan is thereby determined.

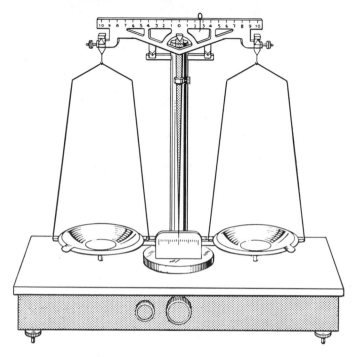

Fig. 4-1. Schematic diagram of an analytical balance.

In unsophisticated discussions, the terms "weight" and "mass" are often used interchangeably, but it should be noted that in reality these terms mean different things. The mass of an object is a measure of the amount of matter it contains; the weight is a measure of the force with which the object is attracted to the earth. The weight is always proportional to the mass, and the units have been chosen so that a one gram mass has a weight of one gram at sea level. Since the same names are used for the units of mass and of weight, and since the two quantities are numerically equal (at sea level), they are often used interchangeably. It should be noted, however, that as an object is moved away from the earth, the gravitational attraction, and therefore the weight, diminishes. The mass however remains constant.

The Law of Conservation of Mass

In considering the nature of chemical change, the first question we must answer is whether the weight of the products of a chemical reaction is equal to that of the reactants, or whether the weight of the reaction mixture changes as the reaction proceeds. Experiments that might throw some light on this question were reported as early as 1630 by Jean Rey, a French physician, whose findings were later verified and extended by Robert Boyle in 1673. Let us describe some of Boyle's results.

It is well known that iron rusts and copper tarnishes in air at room temperature. These reactions occur much faster at higher temperatures, and Boyle found that his sample of copper changed into a new black compound in a couple of hours when he heated it in a furnace. When he compared the weight of the black compound with that of the original copper, he found that the weight had increased by six to ten per cent. When he heated iron in the same way, the weight increased by 25%; when he heated tin, the weight increased by 12%; and even the "noble" metal silver tarnished on heating and its weight increased by one per cent.

From these results one might readily conclude that chemical changes are accompanied by an increase in weight of the material involved. Unfortunately, however, there was a flaw in the design of these experiments: the metals were heated in an open vessel, in contact with the air, and it was impossible to tell whether or not the air had participated in the reaction.

The problem was finally solved by Antoine Lavoisier in 1774. Lavoisier sealed a definite amount of air and metal in a glass vessel and weighed the vessel and its contents. He then applied heat until the reaction of the metal

Antoine Laurent Lavoisier: 1743–1794

Lavoisier's careful experimental work and brilliant deductions introduced our modern views of chemical change.

seemed to be complete and, without opening the vessel, reweighed it. Since the vessel remained sealed throughout the experiment, matter could neither enter nor leave. Any change in weight therefore could be rightfully attributed to the chemical reaction. Moreover, since he used a very sensitive balance, even if the weight change had been a small one, he could have detected it. The balance which he had constructed especially for this purpose could detect changes in weight as small as 0.0005 g. (This is roughly 1/100 the weight of a drop of water.)

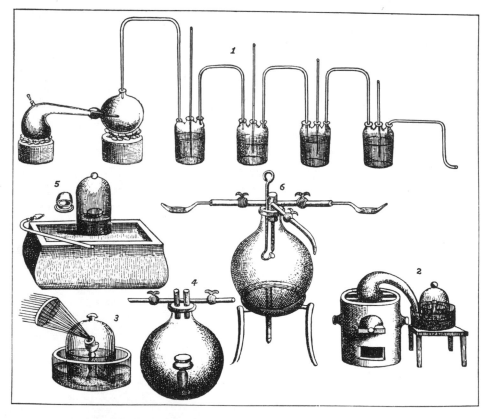

Fig. 4-2. Some of Lavoisier's chemical apparatus. (1) Apparatus for the production of gaseous substances. The desired gas is produced by heating a suitable substance in the "retort" on the left, and then purified by bubbling through a series of gas-washing bottles. (2) Apparatus used in the famous oxidation of mercury. (3) and (4) Apparatus for the combustion of phosphorous. Note the lens or "burning glass" which concentrates solar heat on the sample. (5) The same apparatus, with pneumatic trough of marble. (6) Apparatus for the synthesis of water using electric spark.

In his first experiment, Lavoisier heated a sample of tin above its melting point. The tin tarnished and a black solid product was obtained, readily at first, then more slowly, and after a while the reaction stopped. After the sealed vessel had cooled, it was reweighed. *The weight was exactly the same as before the heating*—definite evidence that no fundamental change in weight had occurred even though there was visible evidence that a chemical reaction had taken place. Lavoisier then opened the retort and verified Boyle's result that the black reaction product weighed more than the tin from which it had been obtained. But at the same time he found that the weight of the air inside the closed vessel had decreased by an equal amount. In modern terminology, what happened was that the tin had reacted with the oxygen in the air to form a new substance, tin oxide.

Lavoisier's finding that the weight of the reaction products is equal to that of the reactants which have disappeared, and that the total weight remains constant, has been confirmed many times for all sorts of chemical reactions, and no significant exceptions have ever been noted. Thus, we may formulate a general rule which summarizes all observations of this kind. We shall call this rule the LAW OF CONSERVATION OF MASS:

Matter is neither destroyed nor created when a chemical reaction takes place; the total weight of all the reaction products is exactly equal to the total weight of all the reactants from which the products were obtained.

This law is fundamental. All of analytical chemistry is founded upon it. Since chemical analysis is being done by many scientists every day, one can truthfully say that the law of conservation of mass is still being tested constantly in laboratories all over the world.*

The Law of Definite Composition

In Chapter 3 we stated that when two pure substances combine to form a given compound, they do so in a definite proportion by weight. We shall now discuss the experimental evidence in support of this statement. Our remarks will also serve as an introduction to the methods of chemical analysis.

The easiest and most direct method of determining the composition of a compound is to find the weights of the elements which must react in order to form the compound. A good example is found in the work of the Swedish chemist, J. J. Berzelius (1779–1848), on the composition of lead

---

*The law of conservation of mass applies only to ordinary chemical reactions, and not to the reactions of atomic nuclei. This limitation of the law will be discussed in Chapter 17.

Jöns Jakob Berzelius: 1779–1848

Berzelius' painstaking analytical work did much to establish the validity of the atomic theory of matter.

sulfide. Ten grams of the element, lead, was heated with three grams of the element, sulfur, until the reaction between the two was complete. The reaction product, lead sulfide, is a black crystalline solid and is easily distinguished from lead, which is a soft silvery metal that turns grey on exposure to air, and from sulfur, which is a yellow solid. Since the two elements and their product are so different in their appearance, it was easy to tell that the lead—all ten grams of it—had reacted completely; no unreacted lead could be observed after completion of the reaction, even with a magnifying lens. On the other hand, it was evident that some of the sulfur was left unreacted. The unreacted sulfur was separated from the lead sulfide by adding the liquid, carbon disulfide (sulfur will dissolve in this liquid, but lead sulfide is very insoluble and is easily filtered from the solution). After all the sulfur had been removed, the weight of the pure lead sulfide was found to be 11.56 g. From these data Berzelius deduced the composition of lead sulfide as follows:

Wt. of lead sulfide:	11.56 g	
Wt. of lead:	10.00 g	*(equal to weight of lead taken originally, since all of it has reacted)*
Wt. of sulfur:	1.56 g	*(by difference)*
Wt. % of lead:	$\dfrac{10.00}{11.56} \times 100 = 86.5$	
Wt. % of sulfur:	$\dfrac{1.56}{11.56} \times 100 = 13.5$	

Berzelius found that the composition of lead sulfide—that is, the weight per cent of lead and of sulfur—is always the same, regardless of how much lead and how much sulfur is taken. If more of either lead or sulfur has been used than is necessary for the formation of lead sulfide, then the extra amount will simply be left over unreacted.

Another method of finding the composition of a compound is to decompose it into the elements from which it was formed, and to measure the amount of each. For example, the compound mercuric oxide, a red solid, can be decomposed by strong heating into its constituent elements, mercury (a liquid) and oxygen (a gas). It turns out that 45.0 g of mercuric oxide upon complete decomposition yield 41.5 g of mercury. From these data the composition of mercuric oxide is computed as follows:

Wt. of mercuric oxide:	45.0 g
Wt. of mercury combined therein:	41.5 g
Wt. of oxygen:	3.5 g (by difference)
Wt. % of mercury:	$\dfrac{41.5}{45.0} \times 100 = 92.2$
Wt. % of oxygen:	$\dfrac{3.5}{45.0} \times 100 = 7.8$

In a third method of chemical analysis the compound of unknown composition is allowed to react with another element to form a new compound whose composition has already been determined. For example, 10.00 g of sodium chloride will react with silver to form 24.52 g of a new compound, silver chloride, whose composition is known as 75.26 wt. % silver and 24.74 wt. % chlorine. In this reaction, all of the chlorine which was combined originally with the sodium in sodium chloride has combined with silver to form silver chloride. The composition of sodium chloride may now be computed by the following slightly round-about method:

Wt. of silver chloride obtained:	24.52 g
Wt. of chlorine in 24.52 g of silver chloride:	$24.52 \times \dfrac{24.74}{100} = 6.07$ g
Wt. of chlorine in 10.00 g of sodium chloride:	6.07 g (same as in silver chloride)
Wt. of sodium in 10.00 g of sodium chloride:	3.93 g (by difference)
Wt. % of sodium in sodium chloride:	39.3
Wt. % of chlorine in sodium chloride:	60.7

Now that we know how the composition of a substance is determined, we are ready to learn a most important generalization:

Whenever two samples of a pure substance are identical in all physical properties, their chemical composition is also identical.

This rule is known as the LAW OF DEFINITE COMPOSITION. It is true regardless of the source of the samples, whether they be obtained from a natural source or be prepared by a chemist in his laboratory, and regardless of the method of analysis that is used. Thus, the chemical composition of a given pure substance is just as definite and characteristic a property of the substance as any of the physical properties, and may be used in the same way to identify the substance.

It is a fact, however, that two different substances may fortuitously have the same composition, just as two different substances may happen to have the same density or melting point. The identification of a substance should therefore never be based on its composition alone, just as it should never be based on any single physical property. However, measurement of two or three physical properties in addition to the composition will sufficiently identify a substance, because the likelihood that two different substances should accidentally have identical values for more than two properties is entirely negligible.

The Law of Multiple Proportions

Two elements combining won't always form the same compound. This is one of those ways that nature complicates chemistry, but makes it more interesting, too. When more than one compound is formed, the relative weights of the two elements which combine to form the different compounds always conform to a rather simple rule. This rule is called the LAW OF MULTIPLE PROPORTIONS:

When two elements, A and B, combine to form two different compounds, the weights of B in the two compounds, combined with a fixed weight of A, are in the ratio of small whole numbers.

An interesting example is furnished by the oxides of carbon. Two oxides are commonly known: the highly poisonous gas, carbon monoxide, and the gas, carbon dioxide, which is usually produced when carbon or one of its compounds burns in oxygen or in air. Pure carbon monoxide may be prepared by passing carbon dioxide gas over red-hot charcoal, which is a slightly impure form of carbon. The two gases are readily distinguished by their different chemical properties. For example, carbon dioxide is absorbed completely by the solid substance, potassium hydroxide, whereas carbon monoxide is not.

The accurate analysis of the two gases was an important problem during the early stages of quantitative chemistry. It was finally accomplished in a painstaking series of experiments carried out between 1841 and 1849 by the French chemist, J. B. Dumas, and his Belgian co-worker, J. S. Stas. In order to obtain an accurate analysis of carbon dioxide, a stream of dry oxygen gas was passed over diamonds which were heated to a red heat. Diamonds were used because they were the purest source of carbon then known. At the high temperatures, the diamonds reacted slowly with the oxygen to form carbon dioxide gas, which was swept away by the stream of oxygen into another part of the apparatus where it was absorbed by solid potassium hydroxide. The weight of carbon dioxide was determined by weighing the absorbent before and after the experiment, and the weight of carbon in that much carbon dioxide was, of course, equal to the weight of the diamonds that had reacted. Thus, the composition of carbon dioxide could be computed.

A sketch of the apparatus is shown in Figure 4-3. The apparatus proved so satisfactory that, with only minor modification, it is still used for determining the per cent of carbon in carbon compounds.

Carbon monoxide was analyzed by allowing a sample of the pure gas to react with a known weight of oxygen; the product is carbon dioxide which was absorbed by potassium hydroxide and weighed. Since the composition of carbon dioxide was already known, the composition of carbon

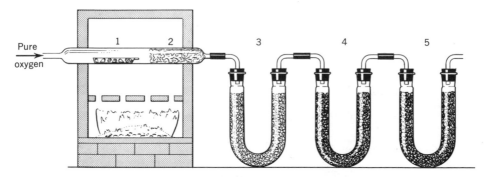

Fig. 4-3. Apparatus for the elementary analysis of carbon dioxide. (1) Platinum boat containing the diamonds. (2) Solid copper oxide, to convert possible traces of carbon monoxide to carbon dioxide. (3) Solid "drying agent" to remove traces of water. (4) Potassium hydroxide, to absorb carbon dioxide. (5) Potassium hydroxide, to guard against access of atmospheric carbon dioxide.

monoxide could be computed as explained in the preceding section. The results were as follows:

Carbon monoxide:　42.84 wt. % of carbon
　　　　　　　　　57.16 wt. % of oxygen
Carbon dioxide:　　27.27 wt. % of carbon
　　　　　　　　　72.73 wt. % of oxygen

Now let us examine these data from the point of view of the law of multiple proportions. First consider a fixed amount, say 100 g, of oxygen, and compute the weights of carbon combined with this much oxygen. The method is as follows:

Carbon monoxide: We know that
　　57.16 g of oxygen is combined with 42.84 g of carbon: therefore,
　　100 g of oxygen is combined with

$$\frac{100}{57.16} \times 42.84 \quad \text{or 74.8 g of carbon}$$

Carbon dioxide: We know that
　　72.73 g of oxygen is combined with 27.27 g of carbon: therefore,
　　100 g of oxygen is combined with

$$\frac{100}{72.73} \times 27.27 \quad \text{or 37.5 g of carbon}$$

Thus, the amounts of carbon in combination with 100 g of oxygen are in the ratio 74.8 : 37.5 or 1.995 : 1. Allowing for slight experimental error, this ratio could be exactly 2 : 1.

Another way of examining the same data is to compute the amounts of oxygen in combination with 100 g of carbon in each of the two compounds. This is done by the same method, with the following results:

Carbon monoxide:

$$\frac{100}{42.84} \times 57.16 = 133.6 \text{ g of oxygen per 100 g of carbon}$$

Carbon dioxide:

$$\frac{100}{27.27} \times 72.73 = 266.7 \text{ g of oxygen per 100 g of carbon}$$

This time the ratio is very close to 1 : 2. Put in another way, there is twice as much oxygen combined with unit amount of carbon in carbon dioxide as there is in carbon monoxide, or alternatively, there is half as much carbon combined with unit amount of oxygen in carbon dioxide as there is in carbon monoxide. The reader will recognize that these alternative statements are mathematically equivalent.

For ease of calculation, the fixed weight of element A was taken as 100 g in all of these examples. It is clear, however, that any other fixed amount would have led to the same result.

There are many other examples of similar simple relationships when two elements combine to form more than one compound. A few of these are summarized below:

		Ratio	Nearest ratio of small whole numbers
	lead and oxygen		
Brown oxide:	100 g : 15.6 g	2.00:1	2:1
Yellow oxide:	100 g : 7.8 g		
	sulfur and oxygen		
Sulfur trioxide:	100 g : 146.427 g	1.497:1	3:2
Sulfur dioxide:	100 g : 97.83 g		
	copper and oxygen		
Black oxide:	100 g : 25 g	2.00:1	2:1
Red oxide:	100 g : 12.5 g		
	iron and oxygen		
Ferric oxide:	100 g : 44.25 g	1.495:1	3:2
Ferrous oxide:	100 g : 29.6 g		

The data in this table are based on the work of J. J. Berzelius. Within limits that can reasonably be ascribed to experimental error, the weights of the second element in combination with 100 g of the first are always in the ratio of small whole numbers.* Berzelius was a magnificent experimentalist. Although, in the hands of some of his predecessors, the ratios did not appear to be equal to the ratios of small whole numbers, such apparent exceptions to the rule proved, on careful re-examination, to be incorrect due to the use of impure substances or due to experimental error. Eventually, before the middle of the nineteenth century, the rule was quite generally accepted as a law of nature.

Only later, as chemistry developed and chemists learned to prepare compounds of greater molecular complexity, did the law have to be modified. The word "small" had to be removed from the phrase "small whole numbers" in order for the law to apply also to compounds with large molecules. For example, ordinary gasoline consists mostly of various compounds of the elements carbon and hydrogen, the so-called hydrocarbons. In two of these compounds, namely in heptane and octane, the amounts of hydrogen in combination with 100 g of carbon are in the ratio 64 : 63.

---

* Experimental error results in part from the limitations in the sensitivity of measuring instruments, and in part from poor experimental technique.

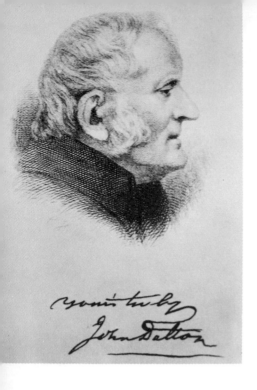

John Dalton: 1766–1844

In 1808, Dalton published his celebrated New System of Chemical Philosophy, *in which he developed his conception of atoms as the fundamental building blocks of all matter.*

This is still the ratio of two integers, but the integers are no longer small numbers.

Finally, it must be mentioned that there is a class of substances, which includes the zeolites and the gels, that are characterized by a highly porous structure and large surface area. Materials such as Portland cement, concrete, gelatin, and water softeners are in this group. These substances can adsorb large quantities of matter on their surfaces, and their composition can thus be varied continuously.

Dalton's Atomic Theory

We are now ready to depart from the macroscopic examination of matter and seek an explanation in terms of a submicroscopic model. The three *macroscopic* laws — conservation of mass, definite composition, and multiple proportions—are all explained elegantly by Dalton's atomic theory of matter (1808).* Dalton's achievement in formulating this theory is the more remarkable when it is realized that, at that time, the experimental basis for these laws was still fairly unsatisfactory. Dalton accepted the

* The word "atom" is derived from a Greek root meaning "indivisible." Originally, an atom was thought to be a particle of matter so small as to be incapable of further division.

laws as correct because his own experiments seemed to confirm them, and because of his intuitive faith in the underlying simplicity of nature.

The important feature of Dalton's theory is that matter is thought to be *dis*continuous from point to point on the submicroscopic scale, even though for macroscopic samples of pure substances the physical properties are uniform from point to point. On the submicroscopic scale all substances are supposed to consist of large numbers of separate particles. This becomes clear when we consider Dalton's ideas, phrased in modern language.

1. *The particle nature of the elements:*
   (a) A sample of an element consists of many tiny particles called *atoms.*
   (b) Atoms cannot be divided nor destroyed nor created.
   (c) Atoms of the same element are alike in all respects; in particular they are alike in weight.

2. *The structure of compounds:*
   (a) A sample of a compound consists of many tiny particles called *molecules.**
   (b) All molecules of the same compound are alike in all respects.
   (c) The molecules of a compound may be subdivided into the atoms of the elements which have combined to form the compound. The atoms are held together in the molecule by *chemical bonds.*
   (d) When a compound is formed from the elements, the atoms of the elements combine *in whole number amounts* in order to form the molecules of the compound. This is because the atoms are indivisible.
   (e) Atoms of different elements may combine in more than one ratio to form different molecules and hence different compounds.

Several of these ideas will have to be modified in later chapters. But for the present, this simple theory is useful, since it explains the three laws which were presented above. First, the theory expains the law of conservation of mass because atoms cannot be created or destroyed. When a reaction takes place, the atoms change their state of combination with other atoms; for example, atoms of oxygen may combine with atoms of carbon to form molecules of carbon monoxide. But the total number of carbon atoms and of oxygen atoms, and hence the weight of the reaction mixture, remains the same.

The theory also explains the law of definite composition. For example,

* Derived from the Latin word *molecula,* meaning "small amount of matter."

in each molecule of carbon monoxide there is some definite number of carbon atoms combined with some definite number of oxygen atoms. These numbers are the same in every molecule, and they are always whole numbers. Since each molecule has exactly the same composition, any collection of them will also have the same composition. Thus, the theory explains the observation that all samples of pure carbon monoxide have exactly the same composition.

Finally, the theory explains the law of multiple proportions. For example, when carbon combines with oxygen, the molecules of each of the compounds that is produced will consist of some definite number of carbon atoms and some definite number of oxygen atoms. The simplest compound will be one whose molecules contain one carbon atom and one oxygen atom. The next possibility is a compound whose molecules contain one carbon atom and two oxygen atoms, or one oxygen atom and two carbon atoms. As a specific example, suppose that the molecules of one of the compounds consist of one carbon atom and one oxygen atom, and those of the other compound consist of one carbon atom and *two* oxygen atoms. The ratio of the weight of oxygen in combination with one atom of carbon in the two different molecules is one-to-two. Since this is true for every atom of carbon, the same ratio will apply to macroscopic samples of the two compounds, such as the samples containing 100 g of carbon that we considered in the previous section, and this explains the observation of multiple proportions.

Chemical shorthand

Dalton introduced the practice of using symbols to denote the atoms of the different elements. This practice leads to a convenient and concise way of representing the composition of molecules.

The symbols which are in use today were originated by Berzelius. They usually employ the first letter of the chemical name of an element to denote the atoms of that element. For example, the letter H is used for the atoms of hydrogen, O for the atoms of oxygen, N for the atoms of nitrogen, C for the atoms of carbon, and S for the atoms of sulfur. Since chemistry is international, the symbol denoting an element is sometimes the first letter of the name of the element in some language other than English. For example, K, the symbol for the element potassium, derives from the word *kalium* which is of mixed German-Latin origin.

When a single letter would lead to confusion with the symbol for some other element, two letters are used. For example, atoms of the element helium are denoted by the symbol He to avoid confusion with the symbol H for atoms of hydrogen. Na—from the Latin word *natrium*—is used for the atoms of sodium; Cu (*cuprum*) is the symbol for copper, and Fe (*ferrum*) is the symbol for iron.

The chemical formula for the molecules of a compound is obtained as follows: the symbols are given for the elements of which the compound is composed, with a subscript following each symbol to denote the number of atoms (if more than one) of that element in one molecule of the compound. For example, the formula CO denotes a molecule consisting of one carbon atom and one oxygen atom; CO_2 denotes a molecule consisting of one carbon atom and two oxygen atoms; and C_7H_{16} denotes a molecule consisting of seven carbon atoms and sixteen hydrogen atoms.

Successes and shortcomings of Dalton's atomic theory

As we have seen, Dalton's theory succeeds in explaining the three laws of chemical change in a simple and satisfying way. Furthermore, it is capable of *predicting* various aspects of chemical behavior for which the three laws of chemical change provide no clue. For example, if we know the composition of a compound of the elements X and Y, and also of a compound composed of X and Z, we can predict possible values for the composition of compounds of Y and Z. The details of this calculation will be postponed to Chapter 7.

So far we have mentioned the successes of Dalton's theory. We must now consider one of the serious limitations, namely, that the theory provides no method for finding the actual molecular formula of any compound. For example, in the case of water, which is a compound of hydrogen and oxygen, the theory predicts that each molecule of water is composed of a definite, small number of hydrogen atoms and a definite, small number of oxygen atoms. The theory provides no clue, however, as to the actual number of each kind of atom in the molecule.

In the absence of a better method, Dalton adopted a viewpoint which is not uncommon in the physical sciences: namely, that nature is intrinsically simple. Therefore, out of the large number of choices open to him for the formula of water, he chose the simplest possible one. Such a formula is one in which there is just one atom of each kind in the molecule. Thus, he assumed that the water molecule has the formula HO. However, as will be shown in Chapter 7, this guess was incorrect.

Laws, Theories, and Hypotheses

The products of scientific endeavor are experimental facts, natural laws, theories, and hypotheses. These terms are used a great deal in scientific discussions, and it is surprising, therefore, and unfortunate that there is no universal agreement on just what these terms mean. The definitions employed by the authors, and probably by a majority of scientists, can now be stated as follows.

Basic to these definitions is the recognition that the human senses have their limitations. If a process or object can be perceived directly by the human senses, a statement about it which has been verified by these senses is called a *fact*. Consequently, verified observations of physical or chemical properties, or of macroscopic processes involving matter, are facts.

A *natural law* is a generalization based upon a large body of facts related to one phenomenon or process. It may take the form of a concise statement, or it may be a mathematical equation. In either case, it summarizes all previous observations and predicts that, under the same circumstances, the same observations will be made in the future. For example, the law of definite composition is the simple statement that any two samples of the same pure substance always contain the same elements in the same proportion by weight. This statement is consistent with all past experience about the composition of substances, and predicts that the same sort of behavior will be found in all future investigations. However, since scientists are frequently redetermining the composition of known substances and are preparing new substances, some of which may be radically different from those known today, it is not impossible that some day something will turn up that is not consistent with this law. If this happens, the law will have to be modified, or restated, or perhaps even abandoned. Thus, the very quality of prediction which makes a law useful to the scientist also makes it vulnerable, for a single inconsistent observation may necessitate revision.

Laws are formulated in the belief that there is a fundamental orderliness to nature so that, under the same set of circumstances, the same results will be observed again and again. Even when observation is inconsistent with an existing law, the scientist is not likely to lose his faith in the "lawfulness" of nature. He will search for a new, more general law that is consistent also with the "inconsistent" observation, or he will restate the law so that it no longer applies to this observation. For example, there was a time when the law of conservation of mass was thought to apply to all the changes that matter undergoes. Then it was found that this law "fails" when applied to nuclear reactions. As a result, a more general law of conservation of mass-energy has replaced it; the new law applies to both chemical and nuclear reactions. And the law of conservation of mass has been restated so that it applies only to chemical reactions, where it is still valid.

As has been pointed out, scientists are not satisfied only to observe facts and formulate laws, but they try also to explain the facts and the laws. Because they are unable to perceive the innermost workings of matter directly, they *invent* possible explanations involving submicroscopic particles and events. These explanations by means of submicroscopic models are called *theories*.

There are certain ideals which scientists have in mind when they invent theories. In the first place, the ideal theory must be able to explain all known relevant facts—the entire macroscopic world. In the second place, it must be as simple as possible. The strict discipline imposed by these two ideals prevents scientific theory from becoming wild speculation. To be acceptable, a theory must be able to explain a substantial body of facts; it will not do to invent a special theory to explain each individual fact. Furthermore a theory must be clear and simple, so that when it is applied to a new situation it will readily lead to an unambiguous prediction; it will not do to populate the submicroscopic world with unpredictable figures like demons or elves whose behavior in a new situation is anybody's guess.

Unfortunately the two ideals—economy of theory and simplicity of statement—are not entirely compatible. For example, a simple pictorial model may succeed in explaining an entire field of knowledge but be unsuccessful when used in another field. If the more general theory which explains both fields is much more complicated and harder to pictorialize, it is advantageous to continue to use the simple theory whenever it applies. Such a situation actually exists in chemistry. The most general theory is highly abstract, mathematical, and difficult to pictorialize. But fortunately, most of chemistry can be explained by means of simple extensions of Dalton's theory in which each molecule may be visualized as a concrete entity, with a definite geometrical structure and a fixed position for each atom. Chemists actually build large-scale models of these submicroscopic molecules to help them visualize chemical reactions.

A theory in chemistry can never become a law because one can never hope directly to observe the particles and processes which the theory postulates. For example, even though there is now a tremendous amount of evidence in support of the atomic theory of matter, the theory can never become a law simply because we can never hope to perceive atoms directly through the human senses.*

Sometimes we make guesses about the behavior of matter which are later capable of being verified by direct observations. For such guesses we have reserved the term "hypothesis." When verified, a hypothesis may become either a fact or a law. For example, a speculation about the chemical and physical properties of an as yet unprepared compound is a hypothesis. After the compound has been prepared, if its measured properties agree with our expectations, the hypothesis becomes a fact. In other cases a hypothesis may be a submicroscopic model which is proposed to explain a limited body of facts. After considerable evidence has been amassed in support of this model, the hypothesis is promoted to the status of a theory.

Bertrand Russell has given an illuminating account of the stages in the gradual maturing of such an hypothesis into an accepted theory: "Every physical theory which survives goes through three stages. In the first stage, it is a matter of controversy among specialists; in the second stage, the specialists are agreed that it is the theory which best fits the available evidence, though it may well hereafter be found incompatible with new evidence; in the third stage, it is thought very unlikely that any new evidence will do more than somewhat modify it."†

Suggestions for Further Reading

W. C. Pierce and E. L. Haenisch, *Quantitative Analysis* (New York: John Wiley & Sons, Inc., 1948) chap. 3: "The Analytical Balance."

T. M. Lowry, *Historical Introduction to Chemistry* (London: Macmillan & Co., Ltd., 1936).

D. I. Duveen, "Lavoisier," *Scientific American,* May 1956, p. 84.

D. McKie, *Lavoisier* (New York: Henry Schuman, Inc., 1952).

W. Tilden, *Famous Chemists* (New York: E. P. Dutton & Co., Inc., 1921) chaps. 6, 8, 11.

L. J. Neville-Polley, *John Dalton* (New York: Macmillan Company, 1920).

* Some scientists, however, have so much confidence in a well-established theory that they do call it a "law."

† Bertrand Russell, *Human Knowledge* (New York: Simon and Schuster, 1848), p. 198.

 *Energy*

SINCE Dalton's time many refinements and changes have been made in the submicroscopic theory of matter. Before we can appreciate them, however, we must know something about the scientific concept of energy; how substances can be shown to have internal energy and how, through their motion and their attraction or repulsion by other objects, they possess kinetic and potential energy as well.

Energy as a Physical Property

Most of us are already familiar with energy in connection with machinery. No machine will run without a supply of energy. In the case of an electric motor the energy is supplied as electrical energy. In the case of the steam engine it is supplied in the form of heat, which in turn is liberated during a chemical reaction. For example, the heat energy required by a steam engine may be obtained from the combustion of coal. This is a chemical reaction in which coal—a slightly impure form of the element carbon—reacts with the oxygen in the air to produce carbon dioxide gas with the liberation of much energy in the form of heat.

Many other chemical reactions also occur with the evolution of energy in the form of heat. Where does this energy come from? The answer is that a given amount of any substance in a given state possesses a definite and characteristic amount of energy, just as it possesses a definite weight and definite volume. This energy will be referred to as *internal energy*. (How this energy is stored in the substance is a topic for Chapter 6.) The internal energy of the products of a chemical reaction is not necessarily equal to that of the reactants. If the internal energy of the products is less than that of the reactants, the difference is given up while the reaction is proceeding, usually in the form of heat that enters the surroundings.

The internal energy per unit amount of a substance is a physical property, just as are density, refractive index, and the other physical properties described in Chapter 2. For example, one gram of liquid water at 25° centigrade and at atmospheric pressure always possesses the same amount of internal energy, irrespective of its history or present location. There is one important difference however: while it is possible to determine the absolute value of, for example, the weight of an object, one cannot determine the absolute value of the internal energy, since there is no way of recognizing when a sample has no internal energy whatsoever. Nevertheless, it is possible to find out whether the energy of a substance in a given state is greater or less than in some other state. For example, it is possible to determine that a hot piece of iron has more energy than a cold piece of iron.

When a physical or chemical change takes place in which energy is given up to the surroundings, the amount of energy which appears in the surroundings is exactly equal to the energy given up in the change. The *total* amount of energy remains constant. Similarly, if a substance absorbs energy from its surroundings, its energy increases by an amount exactly equal to that given up by the surroundings. These experimental observations are summarized by the LAW OF CONSERVATION OF ENERGY:

Energy is neither created nor destroyed in any process; the total amount of energy of the substance undergoing the process and of the surroundings remains constant.

The precise measurement of changes in energy when a process takes place becomes possible in the light of this law. The procedure is as follows: the

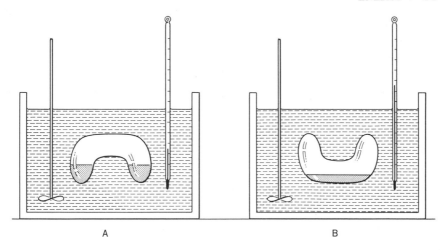

Fig. 5-1. Diagram of apparatus for measuring the energy liberated during a chemical reaction. (A) Before reaction, the reactants are kept apart. (B) After reaction, energy has been liberated and the temperature has gone up.

process is allowed to take place in such a way that the energy received by, or taken from, the surroundings can be measured. The latter is then equal to the energy change occurring during the process.

A typical experimental apparatus (called a *calorimeter*) for measuring the energy changes occurring during a chemical reaction is shown in Figure 5-1. The reactants are placed in a closed watertight reaction chamber of such a design that the reactants can be kept apart until their temperature is the same as that of the surrounding large water bath. After the temperature has become uniform, the reactants are mixed by inverting the reaction chamber, and the reaction takes place. The energy liberated during the reaction causes a rise in temperature of the reaction chamber and its contents. Energy is then transferred as heat to the surrounding water bath, whose temperature rises while that of the reaction chamber drops, until the two temperatures are again equal. This procedure permits the calculation of the amount of energy liberated.

The energy is measured in units called *calories;* one calorie is defined as the amount of heat energy required to raise the temperature of one gram of water by 1°C.* Thus, the number of calories received by the water

---

* From the Latin *calor,* "heat." In very accurate work, 1 calorie is defined as the amount of heat that will raise the temperature of 1 g of water from 14.5° to 15.5°C. At other temperatures the amount of heat required per degree rise in temperature is slightly different.

is equal to its known weight (in grams) times the temperature rise. For example, if the temperature increase in our hypothetical experiment is 5 degrees and the amount of water is 1000 g, then the energy liberated in the reaction is 5000 calories. A small correction must be made for the energy involved in raising the temperature of the reaction chamber, but it need not concern us here.

The experiment shown in Figure 5-1 represents a particularly simple way to transfer energy to the surroundings. Here all the energy is transferred as heat and causes an increase in the temperature of the surroundings. A common example of such a method of energy transfer is the combustion of coal in an ordinary furnace. However, if the furnace is that of a locomotive, only part of the energy appears as heat, and the remainder appears ultimately as mechanical energy of motion of the train. If the furnace is that of an electric power generator, part of the energy appears as heat and the remainder as electrical energy. In each of these cases the total energy, regardless of its form, is the same, being equal to the amount of energy lost by the given amount of coal and air during the combustion.

The preceding examples show that the measurement of the energy change occurring during a process can be a complicated business because there are several alternative ways in which the energy can be transferred to the surroundings. The energy may be transferred as heat, or as mechanical energy, or as electrical energy, or as light, or as sound. In ordinary chemical reactions, the most common way for the energy to be transferred is as heat. Other kinds of energy, such as mechanical or electrical energy, are obtained only if the process is harnessed by a suitable machine.*

Energy and Spontaneous Reactivity

The chemist is interested in knowing the internal energy of substances, because with this information he can predict whether or not a given chemical reaction is capable of taking place spontaneously. If the internal energy of the reactants is known to be greater than that of the reaction products, then the chemist predicts that the reaction can, but need not always, take place spontaneously. An amount of energy equal to the difference between the energy of the reactants and that of the products is liberated and transferred to the surroundings as the reaction takes place. On

---

* If light or sound is emitted and the process is not harnessed by a machine, the energy transferred in this way will eventually be absorbed and cause a rise in temperature of the surroundings, just as an equal amount of heat energy would cause a rise in temperature.

the other hand, if the internal energy of the products is greater than that of the reactants, the reaction will take place only if there is an external supply of energy. The point is that a process in which energy is liberated can take place spontaneously, but that a process in which energy is absorbed can take place only if the energy is supplied.

When the metal, sodium, is brought in contact with chlorine gas, the two will react spontaneously with almost explosive violence and with the liberation of heat and light to produce sodium chloride. Since energy is liberated, we conclude that the energy of sodium chloride is less than that of the sodium and of the chlorine from which it was produced. It follows that sodium chloride cannot decompose spontaneously to sodium metal and chlorine gas. In practice, it is decomposed into sodium and chlorine only when electrical energy is added to the molten salt—a process referred to as *electrolysis.**

Even though we may know that energy is liberated in a given chemical reaction, we cannot predict the rate at which spontaneous reaction will occur. In order to predict the rate, factors other than the amount of energy liberated must also be considered. A study of these factors will be deferred to Chapter 15. To give an example of this kind of situation now, a well-known reaction in which energy is released is that of gasoline vapor with oxygen of the air in the engine of an automobile. Under ordinary conditions, the reaction rate between gasoline and air is so slow that gasoline can be stored in the presence of air without appearing to react with it. The action of a spark plug is needed to trigger the reaction. Once started, the reaction will proceed spontaneously at the high temperature which is produced, and energy will be released at a sufficient rate to drive the car.

The Behavior of Pure Substances as Energy is Added

Energy is liberated or absorbed not only during chemical reactions, but also during changes in physical state, such as melting or freezing. In the absence of a change in physical state, the supplying of energy to a substance at constant pressure always results in an increase in temperature. For example, suppose that ice at $-5°C$ is heated very slowly so that its temperature remains uniform throughout the sample. Under these conditions, the ice will remain solid, and its temperature will rise gradually until

---

* From *lysis,* the Greek word for loosening.

0°C is reached. This is the melting point, and as more energy is supplied no further rise in temperature occurs, but the ice melts instead. Only after all the ice has melted will the temperature begin to rise above 0°C. Since energy is used to convert the solid ice at 0°C into liquid water at 0°C, the liquid must have more energy than the solid. The ice will not melt unless heat or some other form of energy is supplied. When ice is stored in a thermos flask, it will melt only very slowly because the energy required to melt it can leak through the insulation only very slowly.

The same is true of the melting of any other solid. Energy must always be supplied to convert a solid into the corresponding liquid, and the melting temperature is constant throughout the melting process if the solid is a pure substance. Thus, in every case, the pure liquid has more internal energy than the solid from which it was obtained.

It is common knowledge that heat must be supplied in order to cause a liquid to boil. Hence the vapor must have more internal energy than the liquid from which it was obtained. Another example illustrating the same fact is that the temperature of a liquid drops when part of it evaporates. For example, liquid ether is highly volatile at room temperature and vaporizes readily. As the ether vaporizes, the temperature of the remaining liquid falls. This suggests that energy is needed to convert the liquid to vapor. In the absence of an external source, the energy is obtained from the liquid itself, which therefore cools.

The relationship between the internal energy of the solid, liquid, and gaseous state of a given substance is summarized in Figure 5-2, in which the internal energy of the substance is plotted as a function of the temperature. Portion AB corresponds to heating of the solid, where both temperature and energy increase. Portion BC corresponds to the melting of the solid. For a pure substance, this occurs at a constant temperature, and the energy increases. Portion CD corresponds to the heating of the liquid; here both temperature and energy increase. Portion DE corresponds to the boiling of the liquid at atmospheric pressure; the temperature remains constant, and the energy increases. The energy change in vaporization is usually much greater than that involved in melting. Portion EF represents the heating of the vapor; temperature and energy both increase.

Kinetic and Potential Energy

So far we have discussed only the internal energy of substances because this kind of energy is particularly important in the description of physical

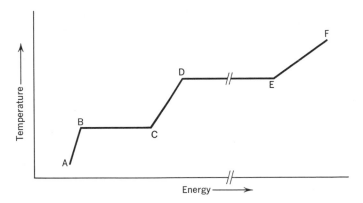

Fig. 5-2. Diagram showing how the energy varies with the temperature for a typical pure substance.

and chemical changes. In the next chapter we shall give a submicroscopic explanation of the nature of this internal energy, and for this reason we must also learn about two other macroscopic forms of energy: *kinetic energy*, which is the energy that rigid bodies possess when they are in motion; and *potential energy*, which is the energy that bodies possess when they interact with other bodies.

Kinetic energy

To be specific, consider a solid ball of steel weighing 100 g and at a fixed temperature of 25°C. This ball at this temperature will possess a definite and characteristic amount of *internal* energy, regardless of its location or speed of motion. If the ball is at rest, the kinetic energy is zero. If, however, the ball is moving with a definite velocity, or if it is spinning, it possesses kinetic energy in addition to its internal energy. Kinetic energy is divided into two kinds, depending on the type of motion: kinetic energy due to forward motion (which is called *translational* energy), and kinetic energy due to rotation about an axis or axle, such as that which a spinning object possesses owing to its spin (which is called *rotational* energy). In either case, the kinetic energy possessed by the object is equal to the amount of work that must be done on the object in order to put it in motion. In general, to acquire a given speed, the work required increases in proportion to the mass of the object; and for a given mass, the work required increases in proportion to the square of the speed.

Potential energy

If the object is moving in isolation, it will continue to move indefinitely in a straight line and with constant velocity. If there are, nearby, other material bodies which attract or repel it, however, the direction and velocity of the motion may change. For example, in the solar system the planets travel in curved paths about the sun rather than in straight-line paths because of the gravitational attraction between the sun and each planet. Gravitational attraction is a general phenomenon that exists between any two material objects; the attraction increases in proportion to the mass of each object and decreases with increasing distance of separation. (To be precise, the force of attraction decreases in proportion to the inverse square of the distance.)

Another interaction is that due to electrical charges.* If the kinds of electrical charge on the two objects are different (one positive and one negative), the objects attract each other; if they are alike (both positive or both negative), the objects repel each other. For a fixed amount of charge, the attraction or repulsion decreases with increasing distance of separation. (The force decreases in proportion to the inverse square of the distance.)

Another familiar example is the attraction-between a permanent magnet and iron filings. Here the attraction is a magnetic one, and again the force decreases with increasing distance.

Whenever two or more bodies are situated so that interactions of the kind just mentioned are important, they possess *potential energy* as a result of these interactions. Just as the kinetic energy of an object is equal to the work required to put the object in motion, so *the potential energy is equal to the work involved in transferring each object from a position far away from all other objects, where the interaction is zero, to its final position in the neighborhood of the other bodies.* If, during this transfer, a repulsion must be overcome, then work must be done on the object. (For example, the object may have to be pushed.) On the other hand, if the object is being attracted to its final position, work need not be done to move it there, but instead the process may be harnessed so that useful work is done by the object as it moves in the direction along which it is attracted. For example, water falling down a precipice is attracted by the earth. This process may be harnessed to do useful work, such as to turn a water wheel or a turbine which generates electricity.

It is important that we understand the manner in which the potential

* See page 90 for further discussion of the concept of electrical charge.

energy of a system of objects is calculated. For simplicity, let us first consider a system of two objects which repel one another. The force of repulsion decreases with increasing distance of separation and approaches zero at infinite separation. The potential energy of the system is therefore defined as being equal to zero when the two objects are infinitely far apart. As the two objects approach each other, repulsive forces begin to operate, and it is obvious that work must be done in order to overcome the effect of the repulsive forces. The potential energy at any given distance of separation is defined as being equal to the work that must be done to bring the objects from infinite separation to this distance. Since work is being done *on* the system, potential energy is acquired by the system, and the value of the potential energy is expressed by a positive number.

As the objects come closer and closer together, more and more work must be done to bring them there, and the potential becomes correspondingly larger. In order for the two objects to remain separated by only a short distance, some form of constraint must be applied. If the constraint is removed, the repulsive force acting between the objects will cause them to fly apart, and the potential energy stored up in the system will be converted into kinetic energy of the moving objects. This process, in which the objects are moving apart, may be harnessed to produce useful work. Under ideal conditions the amount of work that can be produced in this way is exactly equal to the amount that was done originally to bring the objects together.

Next let us consider a system of two objects which attract one another. Again the interaction becomes zero at infinite separation, and the potential energy is again defined as being equal to zero at this infinite separation. However, instead of it being necessary to do work on the objects to bring them closer together, the objects will now approach each other spontaneously, and the process may be harnessed to do useful work. Thus, when the objects have come to any given, non-infinite, distance, they will have lost potential energy; it follows that the value of the potential energy must be expressed by a negative number since it was zero to begin with.

These qualitative remarks about potential energy may be made more graphic by reference to Figure 5-3. The upper curve shows how the potential energy varies with distance of separation when the two objects repel one another, and the lower curve shows the change in potential energy with distance when the two objects attract one another. The important thing to remember about the potential energy is that a negative value is associated with a system in which the individual particles are attracted to one another during their approach, and a positive value is associated with

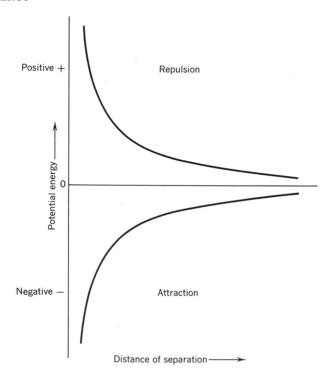

Fig. 5-3. Variation of potential energy with distance of separation.

a system in which the individual particles are repelled by one another during their approach.

This method of calculating the potential energy is consistent with what was said on page 54 about the relationship between energy and spontaneous reactivity. It was pointed out that a low value for the energy means that there is a relatively small tendency for a spontaneous change to occur, and hence stability; but a high value means that there is considerable tendency for a spontaneous change to occur, and the change is accompanied by the liberation of energy. The same is true of potential energy, but in order to see it we must recall some algebra, particularly the conventions about the *sign* of numbers. Numbers can decrease continuously from plus infinity, through zero, to minus infinity. Thus − 10 is below zero, which in turn is below +5. A potential energy of, say, − 10 calories should therefore refer to a more stable system of objects than one of +5 calories. This is consistent with our definitions, since potential energy is negative only when there has been an attraction, and is positive only when there has been a repulsion; and obviously an object is more stable in a position to which it has been attracted than in one from which it is being repelled.

Potential energy is an important quantity in chemistry. We have seen that molecules are made up of atoms, and it is evident that the atoms are held together in the molecule because of some attractive force acting between them. Hence the potential energy of a molecule must be negative; and a molecule is the more stable, the more negative its potential energy.

Suggestions for Further Reading

H. Margenau, *The Nature of Physical Reality* (New York: McGraw-Hill Book Company, Inc., 1950).

K. Krauskopf, *Fundamentals of Physical Science,* 4th ed. (New York: McGraw-Hill Book Company, Inc., 1959) pp. 107–131.

J. J. G. McCue, *The World of Atoms* (New York: Ronald Press Co., 1956) pp. 82–86.

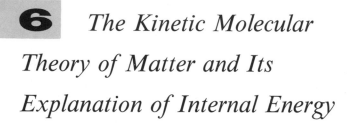

6 *The Kinetic Molecular Theory of Matter and Its Explanation of Internal Energy*

WE HAVE seen that Dalton's atomic theory is capable of "explaining" the weight relationships observed in chemical reactions. Another and seemingly unrelated macroscopic property of matter is its internal energy. In this chapter we shall see how this property can be explained by the KINETIC MOLECULAR THEORY. This theory makes the same basic assumption as does Dalton's, namely, that matter is ultimately composed of many tiny particles. In addition, the kinetic molecular theory makes several further assumptions. It assumes that the particles are in motion and hence possess kinetic energy, and that they interact with one another and hence possess potential energy. The quantity of kinetic and potential energy possessed by the particles is calculated on the assumption that the same laws of behavior which apply to macroscopic objects apply here. The internal energy of a substance is, then, the macroscopic consequence of the kinetic and potential energy possessed by the submicroscopic particles.

In its simplest form, the theory assumes that the molecules may be regarded as hard, structureless spheres. For each substance, the spheres are thought to have a definite and characteristic size, which never changes. When the substance expands or contracts, the spheres merely move further apart or closer together. Why should such a collection of submicroscopic spheres possess potential and kinetic energy?

Let us consider potential energy first. We will recall that potential energy is the result of forces of attraction or repulsion. If we assume that the particles attract one another, then the collection of particles will certainly possess potential energy. In the case of solids and liquids, certain observable properties suggest that such an assumption is reasonable. For example, it is well known that if a given volume of solid or liquid is placed in a container of much larger volume, the solid or liquid retains its original volume. This suggests that the submicroscopic particles attract one another, for if they did not, they would move apart readily and the solid or liquid would expand to fill the entire container. On the other hand, gases are known to do just that: no matter how large the container, a gas will expand and distribute itself uniformly throughout it. This suggests that if the forces acting among the particles of the gas are attractive, then they must be very weak.

In order that the particles should possess kinetic energy, we must necessarily assume that they are moving about. But are they actually moving? When we see a macroscopic object such as a beaker full of water sitting at rest on a table top, it is difficult to imagine that such a still body of water is composed of molecules in motion. Yet there is now overwhelming evidence that this is indeed the case. For example, when a pollen grain is suspended in a drop of water and examined under a microscope, the grain is seen to be moving about constantly in a zig-zag path. A plausible explanation of this zig-zag motion is that the pollen grain is constantly being bombarded by the fast-moving but invisible water molecules.

With the aid of this model we can discuss fruitfully not only the energy relationships of the three states of matter, but also numerous other properties.

The Solid State

Solids have a relatively high density, and are almost incompressible; that is, the application of high pressure will not result in an appreciable reduction of the volume. These facts suggest that the molecules in a solid are virtually at touching distances, and it is therefore nearly impossible to reduce the average distance between them.

It has already been mentioned that pure solids are usually crystalline. For example, crystals of the substance calcite are shown in Figure 6-1. The regular geometrical shape of crystals is perhaps the most obvious, but by no means the only, indication of a highly-ordered inner structure, in which the molecules are arranged in an orderly manner. Such an orderly arrangement of molecules is known as a *lattice,* and the positions occupied by the molecules are known as *lattice sites.* For example, the crystal lattice of copper is shown in Figure 6-2. The individual copper atoms are represented as little spheres, and the crystal is seen to be an orderly pile of such spheres.

Molecules in close proximity are thought to attract one another,

|←——1 cm——→|

Fig. 6-1. Crystals of calcite ($CaCO_3$).

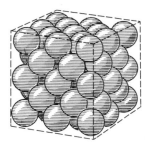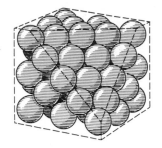

Fig. 6-2. Lattice arrangement of the atoms in a crystal of copper
[after W. Barlow, *Nature, 29,* 186 (1883)].

although nothing has yet been said about the nature of this attraction. Since each molecule has a characteristic mass, we might expect some attraction due to the force of gravity. Calculation shows, however, that the gravitational attraction is fairly unimportant; the present view is that the major part of the attraction results from electrical interactions. This view is based on some experiments, to be discussed in Chapter 8, which indicate that molecules are best described not as structureless spheres, but rather as assemblies of still smaller particles which bear electrical charges.

Now let us consider what happens to a crystal when energy is added. One observes that the temperature rises and that the crystal expands slightly. This latter observation suggests that the molecules in the crystal are moving just a little further apart, and—perhaps more important—that a small number of "holes" are being created. A hole is a lattice site which would normally be occupied, but is vacated as the crystal expands.

This can be only part of the story, however. The rise in temperature suggests that another change is also occurring. According to the kinetic molecular theory, this other change which occurs as energy is added is an increase in the kinetic energy of the molecules of the crystal. The type of motion that is responsible for this kinetic energy is best described as a vibration, or back-and-forth motion, of the individual molecules. A molecule confined to its lattice site is much like a billiard ball confined to a box that is just slightly larger than the ball. Just as there is a little extra room in the box, allowing the ball to move back and forth, so there is a little extra space around each molecule in the crystal, allowing the molecule to move back and forth. As energy is added, the molecules move faster and faster. This increase in the speed of molecular motion is apprehended by us as an increase in temperature.

The Liquid State

The macroscopic properties of liquids are intermediate between those of gases and of solids. Like solids, liquids have a high density and small compressibility; unlike solids, they are fluid, that is, they can be poured into containers of any desired shape and adapt themselves to the shape of the container.

In order to explain the properties of liquids, we shall describe a model that is in accord with many experimental observations. According to this model, a liquid resembles a solid in that the molecules are arranged in a lattice. However, a fairly large fraction, perhaps several per cent, of the lattice sites in the liquid are unoccupied.* These holes profoundly affect the properties of the liquid. In solids, the motion of a molecule is limited to a vibration centered on its lattice site. In liquids, molecules can vibrate in an analogous fashion, but they are also free to vacate their lattice site and move to another one. The details of this motion may be described as follows: owing to the motion of other molecules, the lattice site adjacent to a molecule becomes empty. The molecule moves into this empty site, thus vacating its former site. This permits a second molecule to move into the newly vacated site; next a third molecule moves into the site vacated by the second one, and so on. In time, each molecule, moving from site to site, will have wandered through the entire body of the liquid.

The presence of a large number of vacant sites leaves more flexibility in the arrangement of the molecules and makes it easier to distort the liquid lattice. Hence a liquid lattice is able to adapt its shape to that of the container. This behavior is shown pictorially in Figure 6-3.

Because of their greater mobility, the molecules of a liquid possess more kinetic energy than those of the corresponding solid. Furthermore, owing to the larger number of empty lattice sites, the average distance between the molecules is greater, and the lattice itself is distorted. These two factors lead to an increase in the potential energy of the liquid. Hence the internal energy of a liquid should be greater than that of the corresponding solid.

The Gaseous State

When a liquid is converted into a gas (vapor) by boiling or evaporation, the gas occupies an enormously larger volume and possesses considerably

* Most substances expand in volume by several per cent when they melt at atmospheric pressure.

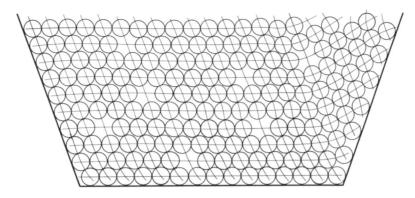

Fig. 6-3. Lattice arrangement of the molecules of a liquid.

more energy than the liquid from which it was obtained. For example, when water at 100°C is converted to steam at one atmosphere of pressure, the volume increases 1700-fold, and 540 calories of energy must be supplied for every gram of water vaporized. This is a lot of energy; by comparison, 80 calories will melt one gram of ice, and 100 calories are required to heat one gram of water from 0° to 100°C.

Although the steam occupies a much larger volume than the water from which it was obtained, it must be emphasized again that the volume of the individual molecules remains constant. The process is *not* like the popping of popcorn in which the individual particles increase in size. Since the total volume increases markedly, yet the volume of each individual molecule remains constant, it must be concluded that the average distance between the molecules is greatly increased. In fact, the gaseous state may be aptly described as consisting mostly of empty space, with a molecule here and there. Such a model will also explain the high compressibility which is characteristic of gases.

How does the kinetic molecular theory explain the large increase in internal energy when a liquid is converted to a gas? The gas molecules are far apart, and we must therefore suppose that their interaction is very weak. This means that the potential energy is close to zero. On the other hand, in the liquid phase, the potential energy is quite negative since the molecules are close together and therefore attract one another strongly. In converting a liquid to a gas, these attractive forces must be overcome, and hence energy must be supplied. During this process the potential energy increases from a negative value to virtually zero. Thus, according to this analysis, the internal energy of a gas is equal to the *kinetic* energy of the molecules, since the potential energy is virtually zero.

When a gas is heated, its internal energy must increase since energy is supplied. Since the internal energy is due entirely to the kinetic energy of the moving molecules, we conclude that a rise in temperature is merely the macroscopic manifestation of the increased kinetic energy of the molecules.

Additional observations consistent with this model

Because of its simplicity, the kinetic molecular model of the gaseous state is readily applied to other observations. Let us consider a few of these.

1. Gases can be mixed in all proportions to form homogeneous solutions. This behavior is quite different from that of liquids or solids, which often fail to form homogeneous solutions. This behavior is readily explained, however, by a model which depicts a gas as consisting mostly of empty space, with each molecule moving independently of all others. There is always room for additional molecules. Since each molecule is free to move throughout the entire container, the impression received by an observer is that of a homogeneous solution.

2. Whenever a gas is placed in a container, one observes that a pressure is exerted on the walls of the container. This observation is readily explained by the assumption that the molecules of the gas are in constant motion. It is therefore plausible that many of the molecules are colliding with the walls of the container at any given instant. Here their motion is arrested and they rebound into the interior of the container, just as a ball bounces back when thrown against a wall. Every time such a collision with the wall occurs, the molecule exerts a force or push on the wall. The vast number of molecules involved gives the impression of a steady pressure.

   The same model can explain additional facts concerning gas pressure. Thus, it is known that the pressure drops when some of the gas is let out of the container—for example, when air is let out of an automobile tire. The explanation is evident: letting some of the gas out reduces the number of molecules, and hence the number of collisions with the walls in unit time.

   Or let us consider another observation: the pressure exerted by a gas goes up whenever the gas is heated in a closed container of fixed volume. To explain this fact, we recall that a rise in temperature is the observable consequence of an increase in the kinetic energy of the molecules. The molecules are therefore moving faster at the higher temperature. This means that it takes less time for a molecule to travel from wall to wall; therefore the number of collisions with the wall increases. Furthermore, since the molecules are more energetic, each exerts a greater force. Both of these factors lead to an increase in the total force exerted by all the molecules, and hence to an increase in the observed pressure.

3. When one portion of a gas is warmer than another, heat is conducted away from the warmer region until the temperature is uniform. In the warm region, the molecules have a higher average kinetic energy than in the cold region. When the temperature has become uniform, the average kinetic energy of the molecules is the same throughout the vessel. This process can not be regarded as the simple mixing of fast and slow molecules, but involves transfer of some of the energy of the fast-moving molecules to the slower ones, speeding them up.

The moving molecules collide not only with the wall, but also with one another whenever their paths cross. These collisions provide a mechanism for the exchange of kinetic energy between the fast- and slow-moving molecules. As a result, the original identity of one group of molecules as "fast" or "slow" is soon lost.

Collisions Between Molecules and the Distribution of Their Velocities

The concept of collisions between molecules is important also to an understanding of the chemical reactions of gases. Normally, the molecules move in virtual isolation. It is the intimate contact during a collision that provides the opportunity for a chemical reaction to occur. Further discussion of this subject will be deferred to Chapter 15. Here it is sufficient to point out that even when there is a tendency for a reaction to occur, only a small fraction of the collisions result in the formation of new chemical substances.

In this chapter we shall confine our attention to collisions which *do not* result in chemical reaction. We have seen that the collisions provide a ready mechanism for the exchange of kinetic energy. However, in each collision the total kinetic energy must be conserved, and if one molecule emerges from the collision with increased kinetic energy, the other one must emerge with a correspondingly decreased kinetic energy. If we focus attention on any single molecule in the gas, we see that it moves with constant velocity between collisions, and that it may experience a change in velocity at every collision.

Another way of examining the theoretical picture is not to follow the motion of a single molecule over a period of time, but instead to consider the state of all the molecules at a single instant. If one does so, one notices that the velocities of all the molecules are not identical, because velocities can change every time two molecules collide.

It is useful to summarize a complicated situation like this by talking about the *distribution* of the molecular velocities. This concept is analogous to that used by statisticians when they talk about the distribution of incomes in a population: a certain fraction of the people will be earning less than $1000 per year; some other fraction will be earning between $1000 and $2000 per year, and so on. Similarly, when we talk about the distribution of velocities, we mean that a certain fraction of the molecules has a velocity less than, say, 300 ft/sec; some other fraction will have a velocity between 300 ft/sec and 600 ft/sec, and so on.

The exact nature of the distribution of molecular velocities was predicted nearly 100 years ago by a German, Ludwig Boltzmann, and a Briton, James Clerk Maxwell, by a purely theoretical approach. Their equations showed that, when a gas is placed in a container and left alone so that no energy can enter or leave the container, the distribution of the velocities will soon become steady. That is to say, the fraction of molecules having any particular velocity becomes constant and remains so indefinitely. The actual numerical values of these fractions depend on the temperature and on the nature of the gas, but the distribution always has the general form shown in Figure 6-4.

The distribution remains steady owing to the operation of the laws of chance: there are so many molecules and so many collisions going on all the time that when one molecule changes its velocity and vacates its position in the velocity distribution, there is a strong probability that some other molecule in some other collision will have changed its velocity so as to take up this position in the velocity distribution.

Figure 6-4 looks very much like a diagram showing the distribution of incomes in a typical society, or like one showing the distribution of grades in a student population. Let us examine Figure 6-4 in detail. There are many molecules whose velocities are close to the average; there are fewer molecules whose velocities are appreciably higher or lower than the average; and there are a very few molecules with extremely high velocities. It appears, as will be seen in later chapters, that the molecules with extremely high velocities (and therefore proportionately high kinetic energy) are the ones that are capable of undergoing chemical reaction.

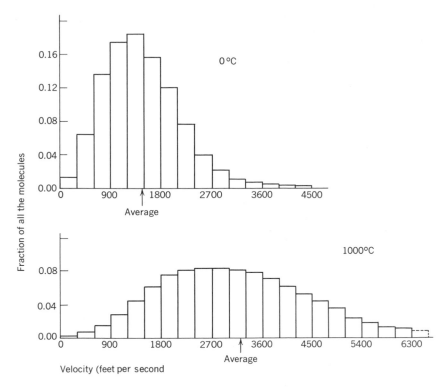

Fig. 6-4. Diagrams showing the velocity distribution for nitrogen molecules at 0°C and at 1000°C. Note that the fraction of fast-moving molecules is much greater at the higher temperature.

Some Numerical Results*

The kinetic molecular theory allows us to learn something about a number of properties of molecules which are not capable of being observed directly, such as size and collision frequency. We shall now present some of these results, without going into details of their derivation. It is fair to say that these results are quite accurate, provided that the kinetic molecular theory itself constitutes an accurate model. They will do much to help us visualize the submicroscopic picture of the gaseous state.

The average velocities of the molecules of typical gases have been

---

* If the reader is unfamiliar with exponential notation, he should read Appendix B before starting this section.

computed from the distribution curves of the molecular velocities for the gases in question. The results are as follows:

Hydrogen:	5540 ft/sec at 0°
Nitrogen:	1490 ft/sec at 0°
Carbon dioxide:	1190 ft/sec at 0°

Average velocities increase slightly with increasing temperature and are about double these figures at 800°C, which is roughly the temperature inside a hot gas flame. Expressed in miles per hour, the molecules travel at speeds ranging from 800 to 4000 mi/hr, similar to those of our fastest jet planes.

Another quantity of interest is the size of the molecules. Some specific values for the average diameter of actual molecules are as follows:

Hydrogen molecules:	2.2×10^{-8} cm in diameter
Nitrogen molecules:	3.2×10^{-8} cm in diameter
Carbon dioxide molecules:	3.6×10^{-8} cm in diameter

Note that the average diameters of these molecules are of the order of 1/100,000,000 cm. Of course, this is much too small to be seen with the naked eye, or even with a good microscope which can magnify an object to a thousand times its original size. The smallest object that can be seen under such a microscope must be at least 1/100,000 cm in diameter, or still a thousand times larger than a typical molecule.

As the molecules traverse the container in which they are held captive, their paths cross from time to time, and a collision results. It is of interest to list the average distance a molecule will travel between collisions. Of course, this distance depends on how many molecules there are in the container, because the frequency with which the paths will cross will increase with the number of molecules. Since the pressure of the gas is also proportional to the number of molecules, we shall tabulate the average distance between collisions as a function of the pressure.

Average distance between collisions	PRESSURE		
	1 atm	$\frac{1}{1000}$ atm	$\frac{1}{1,000,000}$ atm
Hydrogen	1.12×10^{-5} cm	0.0112 cm	11.2 cm
Nitrogen	0.60×10^{-5} cm	0.0060 cm	6.0 cm
Carbon dioxide	0.40×10^{-5} cm	0.0040 cm	4.0 cm

The first column of the preceding table shows that at 1 atm pressure, the average distance between collisions is only about 1/100,000 cm, which is very small indeed. But this distance increases with decreasing pressure, and at a pressure of 1/1,000,000 atm, which is readily attainable in the laboratory with modern gas pumps, the molecules travel for several centimeters between collisions. Since this distance is of the same order of magnitude as the wall-to-wall distance of a small laboratory apparatus, many molecules will be traveling from wall to wall without colliding at all with other molecules.

Perhaps the most impressive figure is the number of collisions experienced by one molecule in 1 sec. This number is again dependent on the pressure of the gas and will be listed as a function of the pressure:

Number of collisions experienced by one molecule in 1 sec	1 atm	$\frac{1}{1000}$ atm	$\frac{1}{1,000,000}$ atm
Hydrogen	1.6×10^{10}	1.6×10^{7}	16,000
Nitrogen	0.8×10^{10}	0.8×10^{7}	8,000
Carbon dioxide	0.95×10^{10}	0.95×10^{7}	9,500

At 1 atm, the number of collisions experienced by one molecule in 1 sec is about ten billion. In order to visualize the enormity of this number, imagine a prize fighter hitting a punching bag at the rate of three times a second. He will have to stand there punching contiuously for 100 years before he has hit the punching bag as many times as one molecule gets hit in one second.

As the pressure is lowered, the frequency of the collisions decreases, but even at 1/1,000,000 atm it is still about 10,000 per second.

At any given temperature, the average kinetic energy of translation is exactly the same for all gases. This is true even though the weights of the molecules may vary from substance to substance, because the heavier molecules move just enough more slowly than the lighter ones to result in exact equality of the average translational energies. For example, we saw that hydrogen has a greater average velocity than nitrogen, but the hydrogen molecules are also lighter than the nitrogen molecules, so that the work required to accelerate a hydrogen molecule from rest to its average velocity is exactly equal to the work required to accelerate a nitrogen molecule from rest to its average velocity.

*   *   *

The kinetic molecular theory treats molecules as though they were unstructured spheres. This model is obviously too simple, for we already know that molecules are aggregates of atoms. In the next chapter we shall return to the study of the atomic complexity of molecular structure.

Suggestions for Further Reading

G. H. Wannier, "The Nature of Solids," *American Scientist,* Dec. 1952, p. 39.

N. D. Cheronis, J. B. Parsons, and C. E. Ronneberg, *The Study of the Physical World* (New York: Houghton Mifflin Company, 1950) pp. 373–379.

K. Krauskopf, *Fundamentals of Physical Sciences,* 4th ed. (New York: McGraw-Hill Book Company, Inc., 1959) chap. 10.

A. Holden and P. Singer, *Crystals and Crystal Growing* (New York: Anchor Books, Doubleday & Co., Inc., 1960).

7 *Molecular Formulas and the Atomic Weight Scale*

The Problem of the Molecular Formula

Once the concept is accepted that a molecule is the smallest subdivision of a pure substance, and in turn is composed of a number of atoms, the question arises as to how to obtain the molecular formula, that is, the *number* of each kind of atom in the molecule. Is it possible to derive the molecular formula from the percentage composition, or does one need additional information? For example, in the case of water it is known that each water molecule is composed only of hydrogen atoms and oxygen atoms, and that the composition of water is 88.8 weight per cent of oxygen and 11.2 weight per cent of hydrogen. It will be shown, however, that this information is not sufficient. At the very least, one must also know the relative weights of the hydrogen and oxygen atoms. That is, one must know how the weight of one oxygen atom compares with the weight of one hydrogen atom.

How can one determine the relative weights of the two atoms? It might occur to the reader simply to weigh an atom of oxygen and an atom of hydrogen and to compare the two weights, thus determining directly the relative weight of the two kinds of atoms. It will become apparent, however, that this simple approach is not practical for purely technical reasons. We shall see that individual atoms are so small that in a single drop of water (1/20 g) there are 5×10^{21} atoms. The most sensitive balances available at this time can detect 1/100,000,000 g, a weight which still represents 1×10^{14} atoms. The task of weighing directly one of these tiny fragments certainly appears to be an insuperable one.

Since there is no direct way to determine the relative weights of the two atoms, the problem of determining the relative numbers cannot be solved by this approach. Dalton, who was aware of this difficulty, decided to work the problem in reverse. He reasoned that if he could make the correct guess as to the relative number of atoms in the water molecule, he could then figure out the relative weights for use in other problems. Believing in the essential simplicity of nature, as it will be recalled, he made the simplest possible assumption, namely, that each molecule of water is composed of one hydrogen atom and one oxygen atom (HO). Let us see how this logical but incorrect assumption allowed him to calculate the relative weights of the two atoms.

The calculation must necessarily begin with the experimental fact, namely, the percentage composition of water. Using this information, and the assumption that the formula of water is HO, we obtain the relative weights as follows:

(1)   Wt. % of hydrogen
        = total wt. of hydrogen in 100 g of water
        = number of hydrogen atoms in 100 g of water $\times$ wt. of 1 hydrogen atom

(2)   Wt. % of oxygen
        = total wt. of oxygen in 100 g of water
        = number of oxygen atoms in 100 g of water $\times$ wt. of 1 oxygen atom

Dividing (1) by (2) gives (3):

(3) $\dfrac{\text{wt. \% of hydrogen}}{\text{wt. \% of oxygen}}$

$\quad = \dfrac{\text{number of hydrogen atoms in 100 g of water}}{\text{number of oxygen atoms in 100 g of water}} \times \dfrac{\text{wt. of 1 hydrogen atom}}{\text{wt. of 1 oxygen atom}}$

In order to solve for the relative weights of the two kinds of atoms, we make use of information given above:

(4) $\dfrac{\text{wt. \% of hydrogen}}{\text{wt. \% of oxygen}} = \dfrac{11.2}{88.8}$

Since the number of hydrogen atoms is assumed to be equal to the number of oxygen atoms (each molecule has the formula HO), the ratio

$$\frac{\text{number of hydrogen atoms in 100 g of water}}{\text{number of oxygen atoms in 100 g of water}}$$

must be equal to one. Note that we can evaluate the *ratio* even though we do not know the actual numbers. Substituting these values in equation (3), we obtain

(5) $\dfrac{11.2}{88.8} = 1 \times \dfrac{\text{wt. of 1 hydrogen atom}}{\text{wt. of 1 oxygen atom}}$

Solving equation (5), the desired ratio of the weights of the atoms is found to be 11.2/88.8, or approximately one to eight. In other words, *if Dalton's assumption as to the formula of the water molecule were correct,* then one oxygen atom would weigh eight times as much as one hydrogen atom.

An analogous method of calculation is used to determine the relative number of atoms in a molecule when the percentage composition and the relative weights of the atoms are known. For example, one of the oxides of carbon consists of 42.84 weight per cent of carbon and 57.16 weight per cent of oxygen. By some independent means it is found that the relative weight of a carbon atom compared to that of an oxygen atom is as three is to four. Given this information, let us calculate the relative number of carbon atoms and oxygen atoms. We begin with equation (6), which is analogous to (3).

(6) $\dfrac{\text{wt. \% of carbon}}{\text{wt. \% of oxygen}}$

$\quad = \dfrac{\text{number of carbon atoms in 100 g of compound}}{\text{number of oxygen atoms in 100 g of compound}} \times \dfrac{\text{wt. of 1 carbon atom}}{\text{wt. of 1 oxygen atom}}$

Since each individual molecule has the same composition as the macroscopic sample,

(7) $\dfrac{\text{number of carbon atoms in 100 g of compound}}{\text{number of oxygen atoms in 100 g of compound}}$

$= \dfrac{\text{number of carbon atoms in 1 molecule of compound}}{\text{number of oxygen atoms in 1 molecule of compound}}$

Then, substituting numerical values, we obtain equation (8).

(8) $\dfrac{42.84}{57.16} = \dfrac{\text{number of carbon atoms in 1 molecule}}{\text{number of oxygen atoms in 1 molecule}} \times \dfrac{3}{4}$

Solving equation (8), we obtain:

(9) $\dfrac{\text{number of carbon atoms in 1 molecule}}{\text{number of oxygen atoms in 1 molecule}} = \dfrac{4 \times 42.84}{3 \times 57.16} = \dfrac{171.36}{171.48}$

or very nearly one to one (1 : 1).

Our problem is immediately apparent. When we know the number of atoms in a single molecule, we can calculate the relative weights of the atoms, and when we know the relative weights of the atoms we can calculate the relative number. When we are limited to percentage compositions, we cannot calculate either. Until 1858 there was no general agreement on how to obtain the required additional information, although a method for doing so was suggested by the Italian scientist, Amedeo Avogadro, as early as 1811. As we have seen, the best that could be done was to make guesses about the number of atoms of each element per molecule, and on this basis to construct scales of the relative weights of the atoms in the manner previously described.

Dalton's guess, to adopt a one to one ratio for certain highly stable and common substances, was as good as anyone's, and was actually adopted by a number of chemists. But since there was no sound evidence for it, universal agreement could not be reached, and for a while the whole Dalton theory was in disrepute. As we will see, however, there is a way to determine the number of atoms of each element per molecule of any given substance, and the usefulness of the atomic theory in interpreting chemical phenomena was finally re-established.

Gay-Lussac's Law of Combining Volumes

The method of inferring the number of atoms per molecule of a given substance grew out of some studies involving the reactions of various compounds in the gaseous state, made by the French chemist, J. L. Gay-Lussac, in 1809. At first inspection the relation of these experiments to our problem may seem remote. However, it is more often the case than not that the real importance of many experiments does not become evident until many years after they have been performed. Too often today emphasis is placed upon research of immediate practical usefulness, and as a consequence basic research, the accumulation of scientific information for its own sake, is seriously neglected. The facts and experimental data accrued in basic research are the stockpile needed to substantiate important scientific theories. Although they also furnish the information needed in the design of the gadgets and processes that most people think of as the goal of scientific activity, these gadgets in fact are just the by-products of our search for knowledge about the nature of the universe.

Gay-Lussac was concerned with the ratios of the *volumes* in which various gaseous compounds react to form new compounds. He began his investigation by causing equal volumes of various gases (under the same conditions of temperature and pressure) to react with one another; he then determined the volumes of the products as well as those of unreacted starting materials (measured again at the same temperature and pressure). By subtracting the volume of unreacted gas from the initial volume, the volume that had actually reacted was obtained.

One of the reactions which Gay-Lussac studied was the combination of hydrogen with oxygen to form steam. It is obvious that this reaction must be carried out at a temperature greater than 100°C in order to prevent the steam from condensing to form liquid water, since these relationships apply only to gaseous reactions. Gay-Lussac found that when reaction took place, two volumes of hydrogen gas (at 100°C and 1 atm pressure) reacted with one volume of oxygen gas (at 100°C and 1 atm pressure), to produce two volumes of steam (at 100°C and 1 atm pressure).*

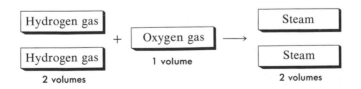

Or again, two volumes of carbon monoxide gas reacted with one volume of oxygen gas to produce two volumes of carbon dioxide gas.

* Chemists use an arrow (———→) to denote the formation of products in a chemical reaction.

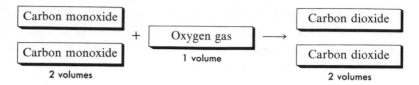

In yet a third example (which was studied by A. Berthollet), nitrogen gas and hydrogen gas reacted to form ammonia gas; here one volume of nitrogen reacted with three volumes of hydrogen to produce two volumes of ammonia.

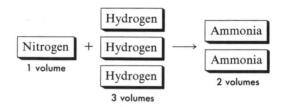

From these and other experiments, Gay-Lussac concluded that

> *when gases unite to form new compounds, the volumes of the reactants and those of the products are in the ratio of small whole numbers.*

This generalization is referred to as Gay-Lussac's LAW OF COMBINING VOLUMES.

On the basis of these observations, Gay-Lussac suggested that there must be some simple relationship between the numbers of particles of each substance involved in the reation and the changes in volume observed. Unfortunately for the immediate acceptance of his theory, Dalton refused to take Gay-Lussac's experiments seriously because be firmly believed the molecules of elementary substances to be indivisible, and on this basis could not see how one volume of an element could yield more than one volume of a compound.

Avogadro's Hypothesis

Another chemist, this time the Italian, Amedeo Avogadro, saw in the law of combining volumes an important clue to the relative weights of the atoms and to the number of atoms in the molecules of compounds. He suggested that by making two simple assumptions, the whole problem of molecular formulas and atomic weights could be solved. These assumptions were:

1. Equal volumes of all gases under the same conditions of temperature and pressure contain the *same number* of molecules.
2. Molecules of certain elements (oxygen, hydrogen, nitrogen, etc.) are not indivisible, as had been supposed by Dalton, but instead consist of two identical atoms which are easily separated when the element reacts to form a compound.

Armed with these two assumptions it becomes possible to deduce the correct molecular formula of, for example, water. It will be recalled that *two* volumes of hydrogen react with *one* volume of oxygen to form *two* volumes of steam. Then, according to Avogadro's first assumption, twice as many hydrogen molecules as oxygen molecules are required to form a given amount of water. Also, the number of water molecules which are formed is equal to the number of hydrogen molecules that are used up because the volumes of steam and hydrogen are equal.

To complete the determination of the molecular formula of water we must make use of Avogadro's second postulate. If each oxygen molecule contains two identical oxygen atoms, and each oxygen molecule produces two water molecules, then each water molecule must contain one oxygen atom. The same line of reasoning, when applied to the relation between the volumes of hydrogen and of water (2:2), leads to the conclusion that each water molecule contains *two* hydrogen atoms. Thus, the molecular formula of water must be H_2O. Diagrammatically, this can be depicted as follows:

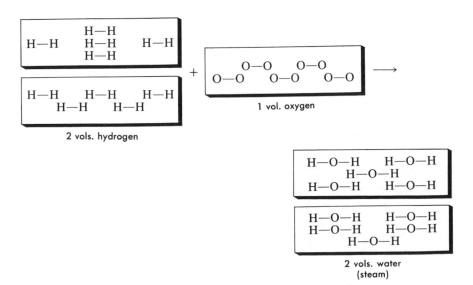

2 vols. hydrogen

1 vol. oxygen

2 vols. water
(steam)

Note that each volume contains the same *number* of molecules (in this diagram, five molecules per volume), and that the five molecules of oxygen are capable of forming ten molecules of water (2 volumes), while it takes ten molecules of hydrogen to form this amount of water.

Postulate number one, that equal volumes of gases contain equal numbers of molecules, is consistent with the kinetic molecular theory and needs no further discussion here. The second postulate, however, does contain a rather arbitrary statement which requires some justification. This is the assertion that certain of the elements consist of molecules containing two identical atoms. According to Dalton, the fundamental particles of the elements are indivisible in character. And yet here is Avogadro postulating a readily divisible elementary particle. Dalton strenuously objected to this postulate and was never willing to accept it. As a matter of fact, on the basis of this objection he cast serious doubt on the validity of Gay-Lussac's experiments. This was an unwise thing to do. One should always be willing to doubt the validity of a theory, but it is wholly unscientific to doubt a carefully conducted, reproducible experiment. Theories have frequently required modification, but a good experiment has universal validity.

Furthermore, Dalton's objections are readily met by the simple assumption that certain substances (the gases mentioned above) under normal circumstances form aggregates of *like* atoms in a way qualitatively no different from the aggregates of *unlike* atoms (molecules) that we recognize as compounds. But why did Avogadro decide that the molecules formed by these elements contain only two atoms? Why not three or four, or some other number? The answer can be found only by a careful examination of Gay-Lussac's data. In all of the experiments involving oxygen, hydrogen, or nitrogen, no one has ever observed that one volume of one of these gases produces more than two volumes of product. This strongly suggests that there are two atoms per molecule in the element and one atom of this element per molecule in the product. If three volumes of product had been obtained, this would have required three atoms per molecule of starting element to provide one atom for each molecule of product.

Later studies have resulted in the discovery that there are some elements with molecules which contain a number of atoms other than two. In the case of phosphorus, which contains four atoms per molecule, one obtains a maximum of four volumes of product from one volume of phosphorus vapor. For example, phosphorus reacts with hydrogen to form phosphine with the following volume relationships:

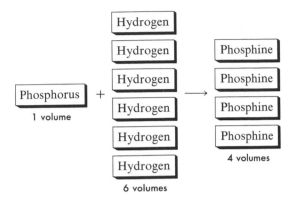

This reaction not only shows that phosphorus contains four atoms per molecule, but it also enables us to deduce the molecular formula of phosphine if we assume that hydrogen molecules consist of two identical atoms. Since six volumes of hydrogen are required to produce four volumes of phosphine, six hydrogen molecules, or twelve hydrogen atoms, are required to produce four molecules of phosphine. Then, in each phosphine molecule there must be $12/4$ or 3 hydrogen atoms. The accepted molecular formula of phosphine is therefore PH_3.

Atomic Weights and Molecular Weights of
Gaseous Elements

It was suggested earlier in this chapter that if the number of each of the different kinds of atoms in a given molecule were known, it would be quite easy to determine the relative weights of these atoms. The hypothesis of Avogadro may be used to determine the number of the various atoms in the molecule of any compound that can be converted to a gas at reasonable temperatures and pressures. Thus, we are ready to set up an "atomic weight scale," that is, a set of numbers which lists the weights of all the elements relative to some common standard. The standard universally chosen is the element oxygen. Oxygen is chosen for practical reasons because most of the other elements form compounds with it. The weights of the other elements are then compared to oxygen. In this comparison oxygen is assigned the atomic weight of 16.000 because this makes the atomic weight of the lightest element, hydrogen, very nearly 1.0, and thus avoids the use of atomic weights less than one.

The relative atomic weights of the gaseous elements—for example, hydrogen, nitrogen, and chlorine—can be established directly by comparison of equal volumes of the gas and oxygen, the standard. Of course, the number of atoms in the molecules must first have been reasoned out from the maximum number of volumes of gaseous product obtainable from each element. Let us suppose that a certain volume of oxygen (under given conditions) weighs exactly 10.0 g. Then an equal volume of hydrogen, which, according to Avogadro, contains an equal number of molecules, will weigh 0.625 g. The ratio of the weights of an oxygen molecule to that of a hydrogen molecule must therefore be 10.0:0.625, or 16:1. Since each oxygen molecule contains two identical oxygen atoms, and each hydrogen molecule contains two identical hydrogen atoms, the ratio of the weight of an oxygen atom to that of a hydrogen atom must also be 16:1. That is to say, hydrogen will have the value of 1 on the atomic weight scale. (Using more precise weights it has been found that the value actually is closer to 1.0080.) The experiment can be repeated for the other gaseous elements and a relative weight—the atomic weight—determined for each.*

Using these atomic weights it is possible then to calculate directly the relative molecular weights of various compounds on this same scale. This *molecular weight* is simply the sum of the atomic weights of the constituent elements. For example, the molecular weight of water (H_2O) is equal to two times the atomic weight of hydrogen plus the atomic weight of oxygen:

$$(2 \times 1.0080) \quad + \quad (16.000) \quad = \quad (18.0160)$$

2 × at. wt. of H   at. wt. of O   mol. wt. of H_2O

The molecular weight of nitrogen dioxide (NO_2) is calculated analogously from the atomic weights of oxygen and of nitrogen (14.008).

$$(14.008) \quad + \quad (2 \times 16.000) \quad = \quad (46.008)$$

at. wt. of N   2 × at. wt. of O   mol. wt. of NO_2

The molecular weights of these two compounds can also be determined experimentally by comparing the weight of a volume of the compound (in the gaseous state) with an equal volume of oxygen under the same conditions of temperature and pressure. In this comparison the molecular weight of oxygen is taken as 32, since there are two oxygen atoms (2×16.000) in each molecule of oxygen.

---

* Using Dalton's incorrect formula (HO) for water, we obtained a ratio of 8:1 for the relative weights of oxygen and hydrogen atoms (see page 77). If the calculation is repeated using the correct formula H_2O, a ratio of 16:1 is obtained, in agreement with the calculation based on the weights of equal volumes of the two gaseous elements.

Atomic Weights of Nonvolatile Elements

The atomic weights of elements that are not gaseous at reasonable temperatures and pressures obviously cannot be determined directly by the comparison of weights of gas volumes. The atomic weights of such elements may be determined by a somewhat indirect method, but one which utilizes exactly the same principle, which is measuring the molecular weights and percentage compositions of gaseous *compounds* of the element in question. Let us consider the element carbon as an example. The relative weight of carbon cannot be determined directly since this element does not vaporize appreciably at temperatures below 1000°C. But carbon does occur in a large number of gaseous compounds whose molecular weights can be determined by comparison of the weight of a known volume with that of an identical volume of oxygen. Some experimental data are tabulated below:

Name of the compound	Molecular weight of the compound	Weight per cent carbon	Weight of the carbon atoms in one molecule
Carbon monoxide............	28	43.0	$\frac{43.0}{100} \times 28 = 12$
Carbon dioxide.............	44	27.3	12
Methane...................	16	75.0	12
Acetylene.................	26	91.0	24
Ethylene..................	28	86.0	24
Propane...................	44	82.0	36

Examination of the last column of the table shows that the contribution made by carbon to the total molecular weight of these compounds is always 12 or some integral multiple of 12. This suggests that the relative weight of carbon, on a scale where the oxygen atom has a relative weight of 16, is 12. This conclusion is, of course, based on the assumption that in those compounds where the contribution due to carbon is 12, there is only one carbon atom.

We can conclude that this is a valid assumption only after we have carried out experiments on a very large number of carbon compounds without ever finding a case in which the contribution due to carbon is less than 12.

Gram Atomic Weights, Gram Molecular Weights, and the Gram Molecular Volume

The basic assumption in Dalton's atomic theory is that when atoms combine to form molecules, they do so in the ratio of small whole numbers. In carrying out a reaction, it is therefore convenient to weigh out the elements in such quantities that the numbers of atoms that are weighed out are in the same ratio as in the final compound. Thus, if we wish to prepare water, we would like to be able to weigh out twice as many hydrogen atoms as oxygen atoms. It would obviously not do to weigh out 2 g of hydrogen and 1 g of oxygen, since the weight of a hydrogen atom is not the same as that of an oxygen atom.

In order to ensure that we are weighing the correct numbers of each, the atomic weights of the elements must be taken into consideration. It is therefore convenient to introduce the concept of the *gram atomic weight*.

The gram atomic weight is that quantity of the element, taken in grams, that is numerically equal to the atomic weight of that element.

A number of examples are tabulated below:

Element	Atomic weight	Value of one gram atomic weight
Oxygen........................	16.0000	16.0000 g
Hydrogen.....................	1.0080	1.0080 g
Sulfur........................	32.066	32.066 g
Carbon.......................	12.010	12.010 g

The reason why the gram atomic weight is such a convenient unit is that

one gram atomic weight of any element contains exactly the same number of atoms as one gram atomic weight of any other element.

Let us say that 16.0000 g of oxygen contains precisely N atoms, where N is some very large number, the exact value of which is immaterial to this argument. We shall now show that 1.0080 g of hydrogen also contains precisely N atoms.

It is clear from the relative atomic weights that the ratio of the weight of one hydrogen atom to that of one oxygen atom is 1.0080/16.0000. Since one oxygen atom weighs 16.0000/N g, one hydrogen atom will weigh

$$\frac{1.0080}{16.0000} \times \frac{16.0000}{N}, \quad \text{or} \quad \frac{1.0080}{N} \text{ g}$$

It follows that N hydrogen atoms will weigh 1.0080 g, and therefore 1.0080 g of hydrogen will contain N atoms.

The same kind of argument can be extended to any other element, with the same result: one gram atomic weight always contains precisely N atoms.

A *gram molecular weight* (or *mole*) of a pure substance is defined in an analogous manner.

One gram molecular weight of any substance is that weight of the substance, in grams, that is numerically equal to the molecular weight of the substance.

It can be shown that one gram molecular weight of any substance contains exactly the same number of molecules as one gram molecular weight of any other substance.

Examples of gram molecular weights for several substances are given below:

Substance	Molecular weight	Value of one gram molecular weight
Oxygen........................	32.0000	32.0000 g
Water.........................	18.0	18.0 g
Carbon dioxide................	44.0	44.0 g
Methane.......................	16.0	16.0 g

The definition of gram molecular weight leads to another unit which is very useful in chemical calculations. This unit is the *gram molecular volume.*

The gram molecular volume is the volume occupied by one gram molecular weight of the given gaseous element or compound under the standard conditions of 0° C and one atmosphere pressure.

Thus, one gram molecular volume of oxygen is the volume occupied by 32.0 g of oxygen gas at 0°C and one atmosphere pressure; this volume is found to be 22.4 liters (22,400 cc). Similarly, one gram molecular volume of carbon dioxide is the volume occupied by 44.0 g of carbon dioxide gas at 0°C and one atmosphere pressure, and this volume turns out also to be 22.4 liters. In fact, the gram molecular volume of all gaseous substances is the same, namely, 22.4 liters. This should come as no surprise if we consider Avogadro's first hypothesis, that equal volumes of gases under the same conditions contain equal numbers of molecules. If we take equal numbers of carbon dioxide and oxygen molecules, the ratio of the weights of the two samples must be the same as the ratio of their molecular weights. Conversely, if we take amounts of two gaseous substances in ratio to their molecular weights, their volumes must be equal.

A further corollary exists. If we take one gram atomic weight or gram molecular weight of any element or compound, whether solid, liquid, or gaseous, it will contain a specific number of atoms or molecules which will be *the same for all substances.* This number, denoted by N, is called Avogadro's number. It is enormously important whenever we want to study the properties of individual molecules.

There are several rather indirect methods for determining Avogadro's number. All of these methods give comparable answers, namely, 6.02×10^{23} atoms or molecules in any gram atomic or gram molecular weight of a substance. This number represents an unimaginably large number of particles. Thus, if all the molecules in one gram molecular weight of water (18 g, about one tablespoon) were enlarged to the size of sand grains, they would form a pile of sand over one mile high and one mile on each side. The immensity of this number is also suggested by the fact that if one cup (about 13 gram molecular weights) of water were thrown into the ocean and thoroughly mixed with all the waters of all the oceans of the world, *every* cup of water subsequently removed from the ocean would contain about 1000 molecules of the water from that original cupful.

When one knows the actual number of molecules in a given sample of material, it becomes easy to calculate the *actual* weight of a single molecule. Thus, if we take 18.0 g of water, which is one gram molecular weight, then we have 6.02×10^{23} molecules. Therefore, one molecule will weigh $18.0 \div (6.02 \times 10^{23})$ g, which is equal to about

$$3 \times 10^{-23} \text{ g } (0.00000000000000000000003 \text{ g})$$

With this information, one can also compute the dimensions of a water molecule. Since 18.0 g of water, containing 6.02×10^{23} molecules, occupies 18.0 cubic centimeters, each molecule must occupy approximately $18.0 \div (6.02 \times 10^{23})$ cc, or 3×10^{-23} cc. Let us assume that each water molecule is a little cube whose length is equal to the length of the water molecule, and whose volume is equal to 3×10^{-23} cc. Then the length of the side of this cube, which is computed from the formula:

$$\text{length} = \sqrt[3]{\text{volume}}$$

is found to be 3.1×10^{-8} cm. Thus, the length of a water molecule must be very close to 3.1×10^{-8} cm. It is no wonder that we are unable to see or weigh individual molecules!

Suggestions for Further Reading

L. K. Nash, "The Atomic-Molecular Theory," *Harvard Case Histories in Experimental Science,* J. B. Conant, Editor (Cambridge, Mass.: Harvard University Press, 1950) case 4.

M. Faraday, *The Chemical History of a Candle* (New York: E. P. Dutton & Co., Inc., 1874).

W. Tilden, *Famous Chemists* (New York: E. P. Dutton & Co., Inc., 1921) chaps. 9, 13.

E. Wichers, "Report on Atomic Weights for 1956–1957," *Journal of the American Chemical Society,* **80,** 4121 (1958).

T. M. Lowry, *Historical Introduction to Chemistry* (London: Macmillan & Co., Ltd., 1936).

But for the scientist it is not only honorable to doubt, it is mandatory to do that when there appears to be evidence in support of the doubt.

Robert Oppenheimer (1950)

8 *The Structure of Atoms: I. The Failure of the Daltonian Atom*

JOHN DALTON conceived of atoms as indestructible bodies, endowed with a characteristic weight for each element, and capable of combining with other atoms to form molecules. How would such atoms as Dalton's be able to combine? What rules might govern the manner of their combination? In this chapter we shall describe some extremely important experiments and observations that will cast some light on these problems. The experiments took place in a relatively short interval of time, at the close of the nineteenth century and the opening of the twentieth, at a time when many thought that the nature of the physical world had already been fully explored. They forced the complete abandonment in scientific usage of Dalton's unstructured atom and produced a drastic revision of our whole concept of the structure of matter.

Static Electricity; the Concept of Electric Charge

A complete discussion of the nature of electricity, and of the many ways in which it manifests itself, is beyond the scope of this book, and is not really necessary for understanding our central problem. There are, however, several observations which are important to discuss because they will help to suggest critical inadequacies in the picture that has been developed up to this point.

It has been known since ancient times that certain substances, when rubbed briskly, are capable of attracting and holding tiny bits of paper and other similar materials. Further experiment demonstrates that this attribute is different for different materials. Thus, when hard rubber or amber is rubbed briskly with a piece of fur it will *repel* another piece of rubber or amber which has been treated in a similar fashion, but it will be *attracted* to a piece of glass which has been rubbed with a silk cloth. Similarly, two pieces of glass when activated in this fashion will *repel* one another. A large number of experiments of this type have served to demonstrate that two kinds of activation or "charge" are possible, and that bodies bearing the same kind of charge repel one another while bodies bearing the opposite kinds of charge attract one another. By general agreement the kind of charge that is produced on a rubber rod by rubbing it with fur is called "negative," while the type produced on glass by rubbing it with silk is called "positive." The unit of charge has been defined, and the law that governs the interaction of charged bodies has been worked out. What concerns us at this point is merely that such a phenomenon exists.

Our theory of the nature of matter must include an explanation for the following electrical phenomena: (1) An object when rubbed against another object made of a different material generates something that we call *electrical charge*. (2) There are two, and only two, types of charge: positive and negative. The simple kind of experiment that we have described suggests that ordinary matter, which is uncharged, consists of equal amounts of positively charged and negatively charged bodies; and further, that charging by friction—that is, by rubbing together the two objects—is simply the act of *separating* the two kinds of charge. Obviously there is nothing in Dalton's theory to help us here.

The Behavior of Gases Carrying an Electric Current

We are surrounded by examples of another phenomenon which throws a great deal of intellectual light on the ultimate structure of matter. This is the ubiquitous "neon sign," a glass tube filled with neon gas through which an electric current is passing. That the neon tube also throws light of a visible kind and can be used to advertise everything from salvation to corn salve is perhaps one of the little acknowledged misfortunes of science.

A simple experiment will serve to illustrate many of the important features associated with the passage of electrical currents through gases as the gas pressure is lowered. Consider the apparatus shown in Figure 8-1. A glass tube about one inch in diameter and perhaps two feet long has two metal plates imbedded at the ends, and is provided with an outlet through which the gas within the tube can be progressively removed by means of a vacuum pump. The gas may be air, neon gas, mercury vapor, helium, or any other convenient gas.

The metal plates connected to a source of high voltage are called "electrodes." If the electrodes are separated by less than one inch and connected to a high voltage supply, say 15,000 volts, the familiar spark will jump the gap. But if the electrodes are separated by as much as two feet, as in this experimental tube, and the gas is at atmospheric pressure, no sparking occurs, and no current flows. As the pump progressively removes the gas, however, a series of spectacular events attends the gradual lowering of the pressure. An electric current begins to flow, and at the same time one sees beautiful streamers of light twisting and turning through the gas between the electrodes. As the pressure becomes lower and lower, the appearance of the tube carrying the electric current changes. It passes through well defined stages until at last, with the pressure reduced to 1/1,000,000 of an atmosphere, the light disappears completely and there is only a greenish glow emanating from the glass in the region of the positive electrode. If the gas pressure is reduced still further, the current ceases to flow.

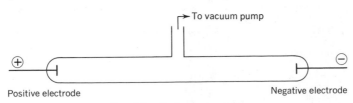

Fig. 8-1. Cathode ray tube.

We are particularly interested in observations made at pressures around 1/1,000,000 of an atmosphere, where current will still flow but only the greenish glow is emitted. The question that naturally arises is: How does the current get across this large gap in the electrical circuit? After all, under ordinary circumstances one must have a continuous wire or other electrical conductor in order for electricity to flow.

A series of ingenious experiments, conducted mainly by the British physicist, J. J. Thomson, led to the conclusion that there was originating near the negative electrode (called the cathode) a swiftly moving stream of charged particles which moved across the void between the two electrodes. These particles were first called "cathode rays" because of their origin at the cathode, and are now called "electrons." They have the following properties:

1. The electrons move in a straight line from the cathode (negative electrode) to the positive electrode.

2. They bear considerable energy, since thin metal sheets placed in their path are heated to red heat by the particles hitting them.

3. They each bear a negative charge of electricity, as shown by the fact that they are attracted toward a positively charged object held outside the tube.

4. The mass of the individual electron is extremely small (1/1840 of an atomic weight unit).

It might be suggested that the "electrons" obtained in these experiments are charged *atoms*. But this suggestion must be rejected on the basis of the

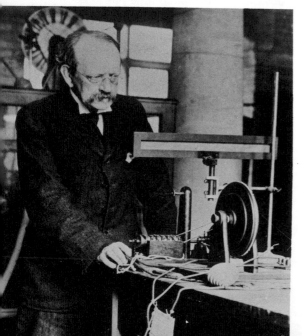

Sir Joseph John Thomson: 1856–1940

Thomson's researches on the discharge of electricity through gases led to the discovery of the electron and isotopes.

following evidence: (1) The cathode rays or electrons are the same (have identical properties) no matter what gas is used in the tube, or what metal is used for the electrodes; (2) the mass of the electron is *much* smaller than that of any atom. If the cathode rays were charged atoms, one would expect them to be different for different gases, and one would expect their masses to be consistent with the known weights of the atoms.

J. J. Thomson was able to determine the ratio of the mass to the charge of the electron, and the American physicist, Robert Millikan, in 1909, determined the charge of a single electron, thus making it possible to calculate the mass. It turns out that all electrons have the same mass and charge. In round numbers, the mass of a single electron was found to be only 1/1840 of that of a hydrogen atom. The charge of the electron was the smallest quantity of charge known at that time, and no particle bearing a smaller charge has yet been found. For this reason, the quantity of charge associated with an electron has been defined as the unit of charge for submicroscopic particles.

Canal Rays

Working with tubes similar to the one shown in Figure 8-2, in which a hole was drilled into the cathode, Thomson observed *behind* the cathode another stream of charged particles that had apparently passed through the hole. These particles were, however, quite different from the previously discovered electrons. First of all, they were positively charged, and secondly, they were massive particles, being of the same order of mass as the atoms or molecules of which the gas was composed. Could these particles be what is left of the atom or molecule after an electron (or electrons) has been pulled out of the atom? That this hypothesis is correct is suggested by the fact that the mass of these particles (originally called canal

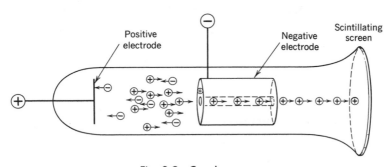

Fig. 8-2. Canal rays.

rays, and at present called *ions**) varies with the gas used in the tube. Thus, if the tube is filled with helium gas at a low pressure, there is produced a stream of electrons moving toward the positively charged electrode and a stream of positively charged particles or ions of atomic weight four moving in the opposite direction. This process may be symbolized as:

$$\text{He} \xrightarrow[\text{energy}]{\text{electrical}} \text{He}^{\oplus} + e^{\ominus}$$

helium   Helium   electron
atom   ion

If the tube contains neon instead, the cathode rays are still the same, but now the canal rays are composed of positively charged neon atoms (neon ions):

$$\text{Ne} \xrightarrow[\text{energy}]{\text{electrical}} \text{Ne}^{\oplus} + e^{\ominus}$$

In the case of both helium and neon, the gas molecules are known to consist of just one atom per molecule. When a gas such as nitrogen is used, which ordinarily consists of molecules made up of two atoms, the situation is slightly more complex but still readily understandable in terms of our hypothesis. Several reactions go on simultaneously. They all produce electrons, but now the canal rays consist of two species.

$$\text{N}_2 \xrightarrow[\text{energy}]{\text{electrical}} \text{N}_2^{\oplus} + e^{\ominus}$$

$$\text{N}_2 \xrightarrow[\text{energy}]{\text{electrical}} \text{N} + \text{N}^{\oplus} + e^{\ominus}$$

In this case, there are formed positively charged nitrogen molecules (N_2^+), and positively charged nitrogen atoms (N^+) produced by the decomposition of nitrogen molecules. Neutral nitrogen atoms (N) are also formed but are not attracted to either electrode.

It seems an inescapable conclusion that in these experiments a process is taking place which violates Dalton's fundamental postulate that atoms are indestructible. These experiments can be explained only by assuming that under the influence of the strong electrical forces, the atoms of the gas are being broken up into two parts: a tiny negatively charged electron, and a massive positively charged ion.

Isotopes

The discovery of canal rays and of the means for determining their masses produced another revolution in our concept of atoms. Dalton had

---

* Derived from the Greek word for "migratory," to indicate that ions move toward the oppositely charged electrode.

expressly stated the belief that *all* the atoms of a given element were identical, especially with regard to their mass. An investigation of the canal rays from a *single* element reveals that frequently the masses of the atoms differ slightly from one another. That is to say, an ordinary sample of an element is a *mixture* of atoms, all alike chemically but differing slightly in atomic mass. For example, neon is a mixture of neon atoms with masses (on the atomic weight scale) of 20, 21, and 22.

Atoms with the same chemical properties but different masses are referred to as *isotopes*. They will be discussed in detail in Chapter 16.

Natural Radioactivity

A third fundamental discovery requiring an alteration of our notions concerning the nature of atoms was made during the same period that saw the discovery of cathode rays and canal rays. This was the discovery in 1895 by Henri Becquerel of the expulsion of various small fragments by the atoms of certain elements. A sample of the element uranium "decays" spontaneously at a slow rate, with the expulsion of fragments called *alpha particles,* each having two units of positive charge and the mass of a helium atom. Other elements decay with the expulsion of *beta particles,* which are identical to the electron or cathode ray discussed in the preceding section. Many of these changes are accompanied by yet a third type of radiation of a very penetrating character which is called *gamma* radiation. It was later found that in each case, the net result of *radioactive decay* is the formation of a different element. Here we see the atom of Dalton literally crumbling before our eyes.

There is much for us to learn from a detailed study of natural radioactivity, but it must be postponed until we have considered the atom and its structure in more detail. The phenomonon of radioactivity is introduced here only to point up the need for revising Dalton's views concerning the atom, particularly that of its indestructibility. In Chapter 16 we will return to this problem.

Rutherford's Alpha Scattering Experiments

One of the immediate fruits of the discovery of natural radioactivity was to provide scientists with a new tool for the study of matter, a tool that has since been used with ever increasing skill and ingenuity. The tiny fragments ejected by atoms undergoing radioactive decay make perfect projectiles for probing the detailed structure of matter. By studying the ways in which alpha and beta particles and gamma rays are deflected, absorbed, or reflected by matter, we can learn much about the nature of the sample under investigation. Further, if these little projectiles are sufficiently energetic, they can dislodge from the atoms small fragments which can be studied, thus enabling us to imagine the structure of the whole atom. This method is analogous to studying the structure of a building by dropping a bomb on it and then studying the pieces. It may seem wasteful, but in the case of atoms it turns out to be one of the most effective methods available.

Very shortly after the discovery of natural radioactivity the three principal radiations emanating from samples of radioactive material were studied intensively, and what was learned about them is summarized conveniently in the following table:

Radiation	Charge	Mass (atomic weight units)	Thickness of layer of air that can be penetrated
Alpha...............	2	4	A few centimeters
Beta.................	−1	1/1840	Hundreds of centimeters
Gamma..............	0	0	Several miles

The way in which these radiations behave when they impinge upon very thin sheets of metals (foils) reveals a great deal about the structure of atoms. The British physicist, Ernest Rutherford, in 1911 undertook a detailed study of the behavior of highly energetic alpha particles (velocity = 1.6×10^9 cm/sec) as they impinged upon a thin gold foil. A schematic drawing of his apparatus is shown in Figure 8-3.

A deep hole of small diameter is bored in a lead block, and a small sample of a radioactive substance which emits alpha particles is placed in

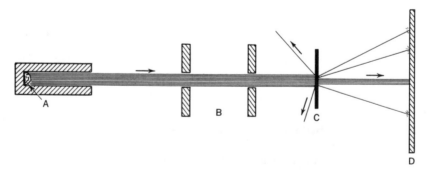

Figure 8-3. Rutherford's scattering experiment. (A) Radioactive substance emitting alpha-particles; (B) lead sheets, pierced with a hole; (C) gold foil; (D) scintillating screen.

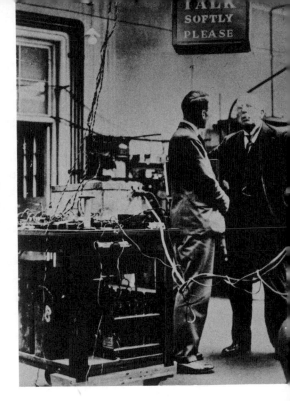

Lord Rutherford (right): 1871–1937

Rutherford is best known for his theories of radioactive decay and of the structure of the atom. He was the first to transmute one element into another.

the bottom. This arrangement acts as a gun which "shoots" a continuous stream of projectiles of subatomic size. Immediately in front of the "gun" is placed a series of lead sheets, each pierced with a small hole. These holes are lined up with the hole in the lead block. Thus, only those particles traveling in a particular straight line are allowed to strike the thin sheet of gold which is the target in this experiment.

Nothing has been said up to this point about the method of detecting the alpha particles which, being of atomic or subatomic size, are obviously imperceptible to our senses. Many devices have been invented to detect free subatomic particles, the best-known being the Geiger-counter. However, the technique employed by Rutherford was more simple and direct; it employed the same principle that is used in luminous watches and clocks. Certain substances, called phosphors, emit light when they are bombarded with alpha, beta, or gamma radiation, and each particle as it strikes produces a single flash of light or "scintillation." In the case of the watch, a phosphor such as zinc sulfide is mixed with a minute amount of radium or some other radioactive substance, and the mixture is used to coat the numerals and hands of the watch. The net effect of many alpha particles striking the phosphor is to produce a steady glow. If, however, the phosphor is coated on a metal plate and alpha particles are shot at it, *each* particle reveals its point of impact by a tiny flash of light that is easily visible in a darkened room with the aid of a low power microscope.

Thus, by placing a large screen coated with a phosphor behind the gold target (see Figure 8-3), Rutherford was able to discern the fate of the alpha particles coming from his source. He first looked at the scintillations *without* the target in place and saw that all were located at a single spot. When the target was in place, most of the alpha particles still hit the phosphor at the *same* spot; that is, they were essentially unaffected by the sheet of gold, passing through it as though it were not there. To the person who usually attaches the adjective "solid" to the word "matter," this observation is indeed startling, and it suggests strongly that matter may not be nearly so solid as we had suspected. To Rutherford, however, the behavior of a few of the alpha particles was even more exciting. For these few, instead of passing through the target in a straight line, were deflected from their original paths as they encountered the target. The angles by which the individual alpha particles were deflected varied widely. Some were deflected only by a few degrees, but a very small number actually bounced back in the direction from which they came (see Figure 8-3).

On the basis of this relatively simple experiment an entirely new concept of the nature of the atom was formulated by Rutherford. These experiments were performed in 1911–1913, and up to that time no clear model of the atom had been suggested. If people thought about it at all they usually pictured the individual atoms as homogeneous spheres which, in the solid state, were packed together in regular arrays. When electrons and canal rays were discovered the picture was modified just enough to account for the new observation. J. J. Thomson suggested that the atom consisted of a sphere of positively charged matter in which negatively charged electrons were embedded, with the number of electrons just sufficient to neutralize the positive charge. His model was rather like a pudding in which are stuck a number of raisins.

Rutherford's experiment makes clear that a "pudding" model of atomic structure just won't work. We already must assume that the atoms are almost touching one another in the solid state. How then could they be penetrated by a particle of comparable atomic weight, if each atom were a solid sphere? And, if somehow this penetration could be explained, why would some particles fail to penetrate, and others be deflected sharply from their original paths?

Rutherford suggested that the observed "scattering" of the alpha particles by the solid matter of the gold foil could be easily explained by assuming that on the submicroscopic level matter is not "solid" at all. He pictured the atom as consisting of a dense central "core" or "nucleus" in which all of the positive charge and nearly all of the mass of the atom are concentrated. Surrounding this nucleus are the electrons, moving around the nucleus in regularly defined orbits, just as the planets move in regular orbits around the sun (see Figure 8-4). The orbit of the outermost electron then defines the geographical extent of the atom, just as the orbit of Pluto defines the geographical extent of the solar system. The diameter of the nucleus, on the other hand, is very much smaller than that of the entire atom, just as the diameter of the sun is much smaller than that of the solar system. It has been found that the diameter of the nucleus is actually about 1/10,000 that of the entire atom.

One can readily see why an alpha particle should have little trouble in passing through a thin sheet of solid matter, if it is so structured. There is only a very small chance that the alpha particle will collide with a nucleus, or come close enough to it so that it is deflected from its original path. Most of the particles will be traversing empty space between the nuclei and the electrons, or at worst they will collide with an electron. A collision with an electron will have very little effect on the fast moving, energetic alpha particle, since the alpha particle weighs about 8000 times as much as the electron and therefore is hardly affected by the collision. The effect is similar to that of a 2000 lb automobile colliding with a baseball. The car is hardly deflected at all.

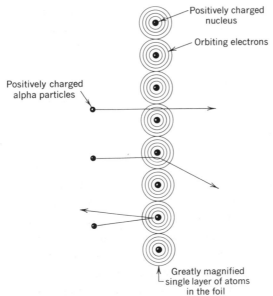

Fig. 8-4. Rutherford's interpretation of the alpha scattering experiment (not to scale). The alpha particles are deflected only if they come close to a nucleus.

Atomic Numbers

Rutherford had assumed in his calculations that the large deflections were due to the electrical repulsion between the positively charged alpha particle and the atomic nucleus, which he assumed also to be positively charged. He could account for the magnitude of the observed deflections only if the positive charge of the nucleus is concentrated in a very small volume, and if the charge is of a characteristic magnitude for each element. Thus, in theory at least, his experiment was capable of measuring the amount of positive charge on the nuclei of the atoms of each of the elements. It was not until 1920 that the accuracy necessary for this determination was achieved by the English physicist, James Chadwick, and by that time several other methods had been devised for the measurement of nuclear charge. These various methods all led to one conclusion: the atoms of the elements can be thought of as consisting of a positively charged nucleus in which the mass is concentrated, and a number of electrons *orbiting* around the nucleus. The mass of the nucleus is roughly equal to the atomic weight of the element in question, and the amount of positive charge is specific for each different element. In fact, the elements are differentiated from one another by the amount of positive charge on their nuclei. The amount of charge usually increases with increasing atomic weight; that is to say, the heavier the atom, the greater is the nuclear charge.

The number of electrons associated with each nucleus is just sufficient under ordinary conditions to balance or neutralize the positive charge, so that as a whole the atom is electrically neutral.

Let us again define the unit of negative charge as that possessed by one electron. The unit of positive charge will then be an amount of charge exactly equal in magnitude but opposite in sign. Using this definition we find experimentally that the charge on the nucleus of a hydrogen atom is plus one ($+1$), that on the nucleus of a helium atom is plus two ($+2$), on a lithium atom plus three ($+3$), and so on, normally in the order of increasing atomic weight. Thus, the nuclear charge of the elements increases by units of one, as one goes from a given element to the next heavier one.* As a matter of fact, it makes more sense to consider the nuclear charge, rather than the atomic weight, as the characteristic property of a given element. The nuclear charge of an element is usually referred to as

* The three exceptions to this rule are Co and Ni, Te and I, Th and Pa.

the atomic *number* of that element. Today there are known 102 elements with atomic numbers from 1 to 102.

A few examples of atoms as pictured by Rutherford will help to make these concepts more concrete. Consider first the simplest atoms, those of the element hydrogen. According to Rutherford an atom of hydrogen consists of a nucleus with a mass of 1 and charge of $+1$, with a single electron circling around the nucleus at an average distance such that the average diameter of the diatomic hydrogen molecule is that found in Chapter 6, namely, 2.2×10^{-8} cm. In a similar fashion, an atom of helium consists of a nucleus with mass 4 and charge $+2$, with *two* electrons orbiting at such distances as to give the atom a diameter of 1.6×10^{-8} cm. Thus, for the general case, an element with the atomic number Z will have atoms with a charge of $+Z$ on the nucleus, and with Z electrons traveling about the nucleus in certain definite orbits.

It will be recalled that all the atoms of a given element do not necessarily have the same mass, contrary to Dalton's atomic theory. While Rutherford's experiments and theory do not suggest an explanation for this fact, they do make it plausible. If we accept the notion that the chemical behavior of an element is determined by the nuclear charge of its atoms rather than by the atomic weight, then atoms of the same element will be chemically identical as long as they have the same nuclear charge, though they may very well differ in weight.

* * *

Our model of the submicroscopic atom is now much more complicated than Dalton ever imagined, and it goes a long way toward explaining the macroscopic behavior of the elements and their compounds. For example, the presence of positive and negative charges within the atom explains static electricity, and suggests a possible mechanism for the binding of atoms into groups or molecules. It also suggests that matter will have properties which we have not yet considered, but which are capable of experimental investigation. Thus, we might predict that atoms could *gain* electrons to form negatively charged ions. Such predictive power marks it as a useful model or theory. However, the Rutherford model as here presented still leaves us with a number of problems. For example, nothing has been said about why the electron is not attracted to the surface of the nucleus, or why the atoms do not penetrate one another's boundaries if they are truly open in structure. These and related problems will be considered in the next chapters.

Suggestions for Further Reading

E. N. da Costa Andrade, "The Birth of the Nuclear Atom," *Scientific American,* Nov. 1956, p. 93.

J. J. Thomson, *Recollections and Reflections* (New York: Macmillan Company, 1937).

A. S. Eve, *Rutherford* (New York: Macmillan Company, 1939).

R. K. Duncan, *The New Knowledge* (London: Hodder & Stoughton, Ltd., 1909).

N. D. Cheronis, J. B. Parsons, and C. E. Ronneberg, *The Study of the Physical World* (New York: Houghton Mifflin Company, 1950) chap. 23.

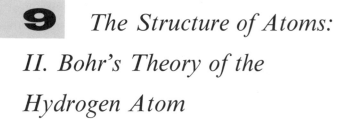

9 *The Structure of Atoms:*
II. Bohr's Theory of the
Hydrogen Atom

Problems Raised by the Rutherford Atom

Rutherford's experiments, during 1911–1913, indicated that all atoms
consist of a heavy central nucleus bearing a positive charge, which is surrounded by negatively charged electrons of much smaller mass. He
envisaged the electrons as circling around the nucleus in well-defined
orbits, much as the planets revolve around the sun. However, this planetary model of the atom raised a serious problem, because it conflicted with
a previously well-established theory—Maxwell's theory of the electromagnetic field.

103

In 1864, James Clerk Maxwell had proposed a theory which, among other things, predicted that whenever one charged object moves in an orbit around another oppositely charged object, the assembly of particles will lose energy by emitting radiation of the same type as ordinary radio waves. (These waves are not necessarily of the same frequency as radio waves, but they are generated by an analogous process.) Owing to the loss of energy, the moving object will move inward. Its path will be similar to that of a man-made satellite which is losing energy by friction with the upper atmosphere. In both cases the orbit becomes smaller and smaller.

If Maxwell's theory were to apply to an electron moving about a nucleus, one would predict that the electron would suffer a continuous loss of energy in the form of radiation. This loss of energy would cause the electron to move inward and circle ever closer to the nucleus until, eventually, it would be in direct contact with the nucleus. In other words, if Maxwell's theory applies to atoms, then the Rutherford atom cannot be stable.

Maxwell's theory had been verified so many times and so brilliantly in the years since it was proposed, that the first reaction of many scientists must have been to look for flaws in Rutherford's work. But the work survived all criticism and the planetary model of the atom had to be accepted, in spite of the fact that it is inconsistent with Maxwell's theory. Scientists were thus faced with the unexpected task of having to invent a new theory by which to explain the motion of electrons in atoms. In the next section we shall consider the theory put forth by Niels Bohr.

But first let us consider the broader implications of these developments. Up to Rutherford's time, it had been usual to assume that the submicroscopic world is merely a scaled-down version of the macroscopic world, so that the laws and theories which apply to macroscopic objects can be used without change. For example, the kinetic molecular theory treats the collisions of molecules in just the same way as it would the collision of billiard balls.

Rutherford's model of the atom throws this entire approach open to question. To this very day, Maxwell's theory has never yet failed to describe macroscopic phenomena, yet it fails to describe the atom! What Rutherford's atom implies is that submicroscopic objects can behave according to rules all their own—rules for which there are no macroscopic counterparts. There is now much evidence to indicate that this view is correct, and much progress has been made toward discovering the rules that apply. Yet in spite of all this evidence, there is still something unexpected, something that goes against "common sense," about a submicro-

Niels Bohr

scopic world that departs radically from the world we know through our senses.

Bohr's Postulates; the Stable Electron Orbits of the Hydrogen Atom

The first person who made substantial progress toward discovering the rules that would explain the electronic structure of atoms was the Danish physicist, Niels Bohr. His pioneering work in the field of modern atomic structure may be likened to that of John Dalton in the field of classical atomic structure. Bohr's theory of the hydrogen atom (1913) is still regarded as substantially correct, although it has since been supplanted by an even more general theory. If we consider that Bohr's great paper on the hydrogen atom was published just over a hundred years after the publication of Dalton's atomic theory, and that now, only half a century later, this work is already considered "classical," then we get a realistic impression of the short life-span of even the greatest of scientific theories.

In this chapter we shall consider Bohr's theory of the *hydrogen atom*. This is a good starting point in the study of the structure of atoms, because the hydrogen atom is the simplest atom of all, consisting of a nucleus with a charge of plus one, and a single electron. Those of Bohr's postulates that are relevant to this discussion may be stated as follows:

1. Contrary to Maxwell's theory, there are certain orbits in which the electron can move about the nucleus without losing energy.
2. These "stable" orbits are a highly select set. Most of the space surrounding the nucleus is "off limits" to the electron.
3. The electron velocities in the stable orbits are in the ratios of integers (whole numbers).

The first postulate is merely a realistic recognition that Rutherford's model of the atom is essentially correct. The second and third postulates deserve further explanation.

Again it is useful to consider a satellite moving about the earth. Such a satellite can exist in a stable orbit at any distance whatsoever from the earth. As the distance increases, the velocity at which the satellite must move in order to remain in a stable orbit decreases. For example, a man-made satellite at a distance of a thousand miles from the earth travels at a speed of 16,000 miles per hour, whereas the moon, at 250,000 miles from the earth, travels at only 2300 miles per hour.

Bohr postulated that, in marked contrast to a satellite which can exist in a stable orbit at any distance whatsoever from the earth, an electron moving around the nucleus can exist in a stable orbit *only at certain distances* from the nucleus. Furthermore, his theory enabled him to calculate these orbits in detail for the hydrogen atom. He predicted that the orbits are perfect circles, and that the velocity of an electron when moving in any one of them is as follows:

Orbit	Velocity of electron (in millions of cm/sec)	Quantum number
First	220	1
Second	$110 = (1/2 \times 220)$	2
Third	$73 = (1/3 \times 220)$	3
Fourth	$55 = (1/4 \times 220)$	4
n^{th}	$1/n \times 220$	n

The remarkable feature of these stable orbits is that the velocity of an electron is either 2.2×10^8 cm/sec (about 5 million miles per hour!), or exactly $1/2$ of this amount, or exactly $1/3$ of this amount, or exactly $1/n$ of this amount, depending upon which orbit it is in. In all stable orbits the velocity of the electron is therefore equal to a certain fixed quantity, or quantum, divided by an integer (whole number). This integer is called the *quantum number* of the orbit. For the first orbit the quantum number is one; for the second orbit it is two, and so on. If the electron velocity is other than one of these "quantized" values, the atom is unstable; it loses energy by radiation, and the electron "jumps" to the next lower stable orbit.

The quantum numbers can also be used to describe other properties of the electron orbits. For example, Bohr calculated that the radius of the first orbit is equal to 0.529×10^{-8} cm. He predicted that the radius of the second orbit is equal to $2 \times 2 \times 0.529 \times 10^{-8}$ cm, or 2.116×10^{-8} cm, that of the third orbit is equal to $3 \times 3 \times 0.529 \times 10^{-8}$ cm, or 4.761×10^{-8} cm, and that of the nth, $n^2 \times 0.529 \times 10^{-8}$ cm.

Small as they are, the electron orbits are very large indeed compared to the nucleus. Thus, if the nucleus were a sphere one inch in diameter, an electron circling in the smallest orbit would be about 300 yards away.

Since the electron moves at the enormous speed of millions of centimeters per second, in orbits as tiny as $1/100,000,000$ of a centimeter in diameter, the number of times the electron circles around the nucleus is very great. For the smallest orbit, the number of circuits completed in one second is 6.6×10^{15}, or more than a million billion circuits! In the larger orbits the number of circuits completed in one second is somewhat smaller, but is still fantastically large. For the nth orbit it is $6.6 \times 10^{15}/n^3$.

There is at least one numerical substantiation for Bohr's theory that should be pointed out now. The average value of the diameter of the hydrogen molecule, as deduced by means of the kinetic molecular theory, was listed in Chapter 6 as 2.2×10^{-8} cm. If the size of each atom is equal to the diameter of the first Bohr orbit, and if we place two atoms side by side, as in the diatomic (two-atom) hydrogen molecule, the long axis of the hydrogen molecule will be 2.12×10^{-8} cm in length, as shown in Figure 9-1. The agreement between this value and that based on the kinetic molecular theory is very good, particularly since both values are based on theoretical models rather than on direct observation.

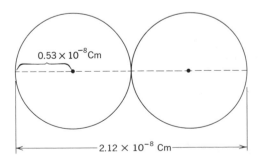

Fig. 9-1. The size of the hydrogen molecule.

The Energy of the Hydrogen Atom and the Most Stable Orbit

The total energy possessed by the hydrogen atom depends upon the orbit in which the electron is moving. We now want to find the energy of the atom when the electron is in any given orbit. This information is of particular interest because we can then conclude in which orbit the electron is most likely to be, assuming that the atom normally exists in the state of lowest energy.

Bohr's theory makes possible the calculation of the energy. The calculation consists of two parts: that of the kinetic energy due to the motion of the electron, and that of the potential energy due to the attraction between the electron and the nucleus. The total energy is equal to the sum of the kinetic and the potential energy. For the hydrogen atom, the results are as follows:

| Orbit | Quantum number | Values of the energy in cal/gram atom of hydrogen atoms | | |
		Kinetic	Potential	Total*
First..........	1	313,400	−626,800	−313,400
Second........	2	78,350	−156,700	$-78,350 = \dfrac{-313,400}{2 \times 2}$
Third..........	3	34,820	−69,640	$-34,820 = \dfrac{-313,400}{3 \times 3}$
Fourth........	4	19,590	−39,180	$-19,590 = \dfrac{-313,400}{4 \times 4}$
Electron and nucleus very far apart..........	"infinite"	zero	zero	zero

* Total energy = kinetic energy plus potential energy.

The preceding table shows that the kinetic energy decreases with increasing quantum number, but the potential energy increases (becomes less negative) by enough to outweigh the effect of the decreasing kinetic energy. Consequently, the total energy is least for the first orbit and increases with increasing size of the orbit. The first orbit is therefore the one in which the electron ordinarily moves.

The Excited Hydrogen Atom

Now let us consider an abnormal hydrogen atom in which the electron is moving in the second orbit, or in a still higher one. Such an "excited" atom is relatively unstable. It will exist in this condition for only a limited time, and then return spontaneously to the state of lowest energy in which the electron is moving in the first orbit. An excited hydrogen atom can be produced only if a normal atom absorbs energy; the atom will never become excited spontaneously.

Atoms are excited by the absorption of light of the proper energy (frequency), or by collision with a sufficiently energetic particle. Excited atoms usually lose their excess energy by emitting light, the energy (frequency) of the emitted light corresponding exactly to the difference in energy between the normal state and the excited state. Sometimes the excess energy is lost by collision with another particle. Both of these processes may be regarded as the reverse of the processes leading to excitation.

By measuring the energy of the light that is emitted when excited hydrogen atoms return to their normal state, one obtains precise information about the difference in energy between the various orbits in which the electron may exist. The results of these measurements provide a perfect confirmation of Bohr's theory. The values obtained by experiment agree almost exactly with those calculated from the theory, which were shown on page 108.

In the light of the foregoing discussion, the reader may wonder if we are justified in using the term "stable" to describe any of the orbits of the hydrogen atom other than the first. It must be admitted that the first orbit is by far the most stable one. But stability is a relative concept, and an atom with an electron in a higher orbit is much more stable than one in which the electron is in none of the permitted Bohr orbits.

It has been found that atoms exist in an excited state only for a relatively short time, usually for less than a thousandth of a second, but ordinarily for as little as 10^{-8} sec. Admittedly this is a very short time, but we must not think of time duration for atoms in terms of our macroscopic notions. Even if an electron stays in an orbit for only 10^{-8} sec, this is nevertheless long enough to enable the electron to circle around the nucleus something like ten million times. In order to convert this to our macroscopic notions of time, let us suppose that a nervous person strolls up and down in his living room at the rate of once every 30 sec. At this rate it will take him more than eight years to make ten million circuits! Certainly a person who spends eight years in the same living room must be regarded as having a stable home address, and by the same token an electron moving for 10^{-8} sec in the same orbit must be regarded as moving in a relatively stable orbit.

*   *   *

If we pause to examine Bohr's postulates, we find that they depart from the laws of the macroscopic world in a rather puzzling way. It is relatively easy to see the need for the postulate that electrons can move about the nucleus in stable, radiationless orbits, because this is consistent with Rutherford's model of the atom and rests on solid experimental ground. But the postulate that only certain discrete orbits are stable is completely at odds with macroscopic experience concerning macroscopic satellites, and the postulate that the stable orbits are related in terms of whole numbers must seem like black magic. Yet in spite of their arbitrary flavor, these postulates enable us to explain an impressive body of experimental data. Furthermore, the same general idea that submicroscopic properties can have only certain quantized values has been extended with considerable success to the entire submicroscopic world. For this reason, the next generation may be quite ready to accept these ideas intuitively, just as our generation has been ready to accept the concept of atoms.

Suggestions for Further Reading

E. Schrödinger, "What is Matter?" *Scientific American,* Sept. 1953, p. 52.

J. H. Rush, "The Speed of Light," *Scientific American,* Aug. 1955, p. 62.

J. J. G. McCue, *The World of Atoms* (New York: Ronald Press Co., 1956) chaps. 51, 52.

Niels Bohr, *Atomic Physics and Human Knowledge* (New York: John Wiley & Sons, Inc., 1958).

10 *Families of Elements and the Periodic Chart*

BEFORE considering the electronic structure of atoms that are more complicated than hydrogen, we need to have additional information about their chemical properties, in order to have an experimental basis for any theories that may be developed. When we examine the properties of the 102 chemical elements, we find a bewildering array of reactions and compounds. However, it is possible to bring some order to this chaotic state of affairs by classifying the elements according to the types of reaction they undergo and the formulas of the compounds that are obtained.

To begin with, we note that there are two broad classes of elements: metals and nonmetals. Metals do not usually combine with other metals but form compounds readily with nonmetals. On the other hand, nonmetals react not only with metals, but also with other nonmetals.

Metals can be distinguished easily from nonmetals by their physical properties: freshly cut metal surfaces have a characteristic lustre, and metals are good conductors of heat and electricity. Well-known metallic elements are iron, nickel, chromium, copper, tin, aluminum, magnesium, silver, gold, and platinum. These are all solids at room temperature. A well-known metal that is liquid at room temperature is mercury or "quicksilver," which is commonly used by dentists for making silver amalgam, and in clinical thermometers. Less well known are such reactive metals as sodium, postassium, and calcium. These corrode too quickly for use in the open air.

The nonmetals include the gases of the atmosphere: nitrogen, oxygen, and argon. Other nonmetals that we have already mentioned are chlorine, bromine, sulfur, carbon, and phosphorus. The nonmetals are poor conductors of heat and electricity; and when they are in the solid state, they are usually brittle.

Families of Elements

It was discovered as early as 1820 that certain of the elements can be classified into *families* on the basis of their very similar chemical properties. For example, the nonmetals chlorine and bromine both belong to a family known as the *halogens*.* Not only do chlorine and bromine react with the same substances, but the molecular formulas of the reaction products are analogous. Both react with sodium to produce the compounds $NaCl$ and $NaBr$; both form similar compounds with carbon, CCl_4 and CBr_4; both react with mercury to form not one but two different compounds: $HgCl_2$ and Hg_2Cl_2, $HgBr_2$ and Hg_2Br_2; and both react with hydrogen to form HCl and HBr. The list can be extended almost indefinitely. On the other hand, few cases are known in which one of these two halogens reacts and the other does not. Therefore it can be stated as a nearly general rule that when chlorine reacts with a given substance, so does bromine; and the molecular formula of the bromine compound can be obtained from that of the chlorine compound by merely writing the symbols for bromine atoms instead of chlorine atoms.

This generalization is enormously valuable. Suppose that chlorine is known to react with metallic calcium to form the compound calcium chloride, $CaCl_2$. Then we may predict with reasonable assurance that bromine

* From a Greek root meaning "salt producers."

will also react with calcium, and that the molecular formula of the compound will be $CaBr_2$—not CaBr, or $CaBr_3$, or Ca_2Br, but specifically $CaBr_2$.

For contrast, let us consider two elements which *do not* belong to the same family, such as chlorine and nitrogen. Both elements can be made to react with hydrogen, but while chlorine forms only a single stable compound whose formula is HCl, nitrogen forms a number of stable compounds, among them NH_3 (ammonia), HN_3 (hydrazoic acid), and N_2H_4 (hydrazine), but not the analogous compound HN. Chlorine reacts with sodium to form the very stable salt sodium chloride, NaCl, whereas the most stable compound of sodium and nitrogen, sodium azide, has the formula NaN_3. Chlorine reacts with phosphorous to form PCl_3 and PCl_5, but no stable compound containing only phosphorous and nitrogen is known.

These remarks may be generalized as follows:

1. When one of the elements in a family reacts (or fails to react) with a given substance, then all the others will probably do so also.
2. The molecular formulas of the compounds formed from the elements of a given family are similar.
3. When a *compound* of one of the elements of the family reacts with a given substance, then the analogous compounds of the other element in the family will probably react also, and the molecular formulas of the reaction products will be similar.

The existence of families of elements greatly simplifies the task of learning chemistry. If we know the reactions of just one member of each family and the names of the other members, then we can predict by analogy the reactions of all the members of all the families. Thus it is possible for an ordinary person to memorize enough selected facts so that he can predict a rather impressive amount of chemistry.

It turns out that about half of the elements can be classified into eight well-defined families. The remaining elements, which are not included in these eight families, are all metallic in character. In the next few pages we shall give a short summary of four of the well-defined families of elements.

The alkali metals

The so-called *alkalis,* potash and soda, have been known since ancient times. Soda (sodium carbonate) was gained primarily from mineral sources —for example, it could be leached from small alkaline hillocks in the fields around Smyrna and Ephesus in Asia Minor. The detergent property of this alkali is mentioned even in the Bible.* Potash (potassium carbonate) was obtained primarily from the ash of certain plants. These substances have been important raw materials in the manufacture of glass.

In 1807 Sir Humphry Davy succeeded in preparing the pure alkali metals—which he named "potassium" (from potash) and "sodium" (from soda)—by the electrolysis of the slightly moist alkalis. The metals proved to be extremely reactive; they corroded rapidly in air and gave a vigorous reaction with water. The other alkali metals were discovered somewhat later. The element lithium was discovered by the Swedish chemist, J. H. Arfwedson, in 1817, and the pure metal was prepared in sufficient quantity for the study of its physical properties by the Germans, R. W. Bunsen and A. Mathiessen, in 1855. The elements cesium and rubidium were discovered by Bunsen and G. R. Kirchhoff in 1860–61. The alkali metals and some of their properties are shown in the table.

THE ALKALI METALS

Name	Symbol	Atomic number	Atomic weight	Melting point (C)	Boiling point (C)	Atomic radius (cm)
Lithium.........	Li	3	6.940	186°	1,336°	1.55×10^{-8}
Sodium..........	Na	11	22.997	97.5°	880°	1.90×10^{-8}
Potassium........	K	19	39.096	62.3°	760°	2.35×10^{-8}
Rubidium........	Rb	37	85.48	38.5°	700°	2.48×10^{-8}
Cesium..........	Cs	55	132.91	28.5°	670°	2.67×10^{-8}

The reader will note that the physical properties vary in a regular manner as the atomic weight of the element increases. A regular variation of properties with increasing atomic weight is not uncommon for the elements of a given family and may be used to predict approximate values for unknown properties. For example, if the melting point of rubidium were not already known, one might have guessed that it must lie between the melting point of potassium and that of cesium, probably in the neighborhood of 45°C, in fair agreement with the actual value.

The formulas and names of typical compounds of the alkali metals are exemplified by some compounds of sodium:

$NaCl$ sodium chloride (common table salt)
$NaOH$ sodium hydroxide (caustic soda)
Na_2CO_3 sodium carbonate (soda)
$NaHCO_3$ sodium hydrogen carbonate (baking soda, bicarbonate of soda)
Cs_2O cesium oxide

* "For though thou wash thee with nitre [archaic term for sodium carbonate] and take thee much sope, yet thine iniquity is marked before me." Jeremiah 2:22.

The other alkali metals form analogous compounds; for example, compounds of the formula $LiCl$, Rb_2CO_3, KOH are all known to be stable.

It is customary that new elements be named by their discoverers, although the name is eventually approved by an official international organization such as the International Union of Chemistry. An element is not officially "discovered" until the proof of its existence is such as to satisfy even the most conservative members of the profession. In the nineteenth century it was considered necessary to isolate enough of the new element so that its atomic weight and a few of its properties could be determined. Thus, to prove the existence of one of the less abundant elements, it was necessary to subject hundreds of pounds of ore to chemical separation procedures in order to isolate a precious gram or so of the new element. Nowadays this requirement is regarded as too stringent because all of the stable, naturally occurring elements have by now been discovered. Any new elements must be prepared artificially, and since these are all radioactive, they will exist only for a limited time. In the case of the element mendelevium (atomic number 101), discovery was officially acknowledged after only a hundred or so *atoms* had been prepared.

There are few systematic rules concerning the names of the elements. The names of metals end in *-um* or *-ium* except for certain metals, like copper, iron, and tin, that have been known since ancient times. Potassium and sodium were named after the materials from which they were obtained. Lithium was named after a Greek root meaning "stone" to acknowledge its isolation from mineral sources. Rubidium (meaning red) and cesium (meaning blue) were named after the color of the light which these elements emit when they are in the gaseous state at a high temperature. Some elements are named in honor of countries, like germanium for Germany or scandium for Scandinavia; others in honor of cities, like berkelium for Berkeley. Still others are named in honor of people, like curium for the investigators of radioactivity, Pierre and Marie Curie. Occasionally elements are named for mythological figures such as promethium for Prometheus who, according to the myth, stole fire from the gods for the benefit of mankind and was sentenced for this crime to eternal agony.

The alkaline earth metals

Several compounds with properties similar to those of potash and soda have been known for centuries, but the metals obtained from them clearly are not alkali metals, but belong to another family and are called *alkaline earth metals.* The alkaline earth metals are less reactive than the alkali metals, have higher melting points, and are harder and stronger. The metals and some of their properties are shown in the table.

THE ALKALINE EARTH METALS

Name	Symbol	Atomic number	Atomic weight	Melting point (C)	Boiling point (C)	Atomic radius (cm)
Beryllium.........	Be	4	9.02	1,350°	≈1,600°	1.12×10^{-8}
Magnesium.......	Mg	12	24.32	651°	1,110°	1.60×10^{-8}
Calcium..........	Ca	20	40.08	810°	1,170°	1.97×10^{-8}
Strontium........	Sr	38	87.63	800°	1,150°	2.15×10^{-8}
Barium...........	Ba	56	137.36	850°	1,140°	2.22×10^{-8}
Radium..........	Ra	88	226.05	960°	1,140°	...

* The symbol ≈ means "approximately equal to."

Magnesium, calcium, strontium and barium were first prepared by Sir Humphry Davy in 1808. Beryllium was isolated in 1828 independently by F. Wöhler and A. A. B. Bussy. The radioactive element radium was discovered by Pierre and Marie Curie in 1898.

The formulas and names of some typical compounds of the alkaline earth metals are illustrated by the following compounds of calcium:

$CaCl_2$ calcium chloride

$CaCO_3$ calcium carbonate—marble consists of calcium carbonate, and limestone is a rock composed mainly of this substance

CaO calcium oxide (quicklime)

$Ca(OH)_2$ calcium hydroxide (slaked lime)

$CaSO_4$ calcium sulfate—gypsum and plaster of Paris are compounds consisting of calcium sulfate and water

CaC_2 calcium carbide—obtained when calcium oxide is heated with coke (carbon)

The other alkaline earth metals form analogous compounds; for example, MgO (magnesium oxide or magnesia), $BaSO_4$, $BeCl_2$, $SrCO_3$ are known to be stable compounds.

The halogens

The halogens are among the most active of the nonmetals and will form compounds with all but a few of the other elements. A list of the halogens and of some of their properties is given in the table.

THE HALOGENS

Name	Symbol	Atomic number	Atomic weight	Melting point (C)	Boiling point (C)	Radius of free atom (cm)
Fluorine.........	F	9	19.00	−223°	−187°	1.35×10^{-8}
Chlorine........	Cl	17	35.46	−101.6°	−34.6°	1.80×10^{-8}
Bromine.........	Br	35	79.92	−7.3°	58.7°	1.95×10^{-8}
Iodine...........	I	53	126.92	113.5°	184°	2.15×10^{-8}

Fluorine is a pale yellow gas at room temperature; chlorine is a greenish-yellow gas. Bromine is a dark red liquid, and iodine is a greyish-black solid. Chlorine was first prepared in 1774 by C. W. Scheele in Sweden, and was shown to be an element by Sir Humphry Davy in 1807. Iodine was discovered by B. Courtois soon thereafter (in 1811), and bromine was discovered in 1826 independently by A. J. Balard and by Carl Löwig, both being young students at the time. The discovery of fluorine took place much later because this gas is extremely reactive and therefore dangerous to handle and difficult to prepare. It is also very poisonous, and at least two competent chemists are known to have died while attempting to prepare it. Fluorine was finally obtained in 1886 by the French chemist, Henri Moissan, from the electrolysis of potassium fluoride dissolved in hydrogen fluoride at a low temperature in apparatus made entirely of the precious metal platinum. The use of platinum was necessary because hydrogen fluoride will dissolve glass. If fluorine were not so difficult to handle, it would make an outstanding rocket fuel because of the large amount of energy released when it reacts with other substances.

The formulas and names of some of the compounds of the halogens are illustrated by the following compounds of chlorine:

$CsCl$ cesium chloride—this salt is sometimes used to make prisms and windows for certain optical instruments

$AlCl_3$ aluminum chloride—an important chemical catalyst

$SnCl_4$ stannic chloride

PCl_3 phosphorous trichloride

PCl_5 phosphorous pentachloride

S_2Cl_2 sulfur monochloride

ICl iodine chloride

The reactivity of the halogens usually decreases in the order fluorine, chlorine, bromine, iodine. The reactivity of compounds of the halogens often varies in the opposite order. For example, the compound CH_3Cl is less reactive than CH_3Br.

The inert gases

There is a family of elements, the *inert gases,* which are so unreactive that no stable compounds of these elements exist. The names and properties of the inert gases are shown in the table.

THE INERT GASES

Name	Symbol	Atomic number	Atomic weight	Melting point (C)	Boiling point (C)	Atomic radius (cm)
Helium...........	He	2	4.003	$-272°$	$-268.9°$	0.8×10^{-8}
Neon.............	Ne	10	20.183	$-248.67°$	$-245.9°$	1.1×10^{-8}
Argon...........	Ar	18	39.944	$-189.2°$	$-185.7°$	1.5×10^{-8}
Krypton.........	Kr	36	83.7	$-157°$	$-152.9°$	1.7×10^{-8}
Xenon...........	Xe	54	131.3	$-112°$	$-107.1°$	1.9×10^{-8}
Radon...........	Rn	86	222	$-71°$	$-61.8°$	$\cdots$

The first inert gas to be discovered was argon, a constituent of the atmosphere making up about 1 per cent of ordinary air. The discovery took place in 1894, fairly late in the history of the discovery of the stable elements, and the credit for it goes to Lord Rayleigh and Sir William Ramsay. The story of the discovery of argon is of interest because it is a good example of research that was free to investigate unexpected and startling phenomena when they turned up. Lord Rayleigh was investigating the atomic weight of nitrogen, and in this connection prepared the gas by three different methods. One of the methods he used was to separate nitrogen from the other components of the atmosphere. He subjected ordinary air to various chemical procedures until he ended up with a gas that should have been pure nitrogen. But to his consternation, the density of this gas was just slightly different from that of samples prepared by the other methods, one of which was the decomposition of ammonia. Guided by some experiments carried out by the British scientist, Henry Cavendish, more than a hundred years earlier, Rayleigh suspected that the "nitrogen" obtained from ordinary air still contained an impurity. Collaborating with Ramsay, he subjected the gas to all sorts of chemical procedures that were designed to remove any and all conceivable impurities. When all of these failed, Ramsay decided to abandon the original investigation and to study the impurity. He passed the impure nitrogen over hot magnesium, which removed the nitrogen gas by forming solid magnesium nitride, Mg_3N_2. A small amount of gas was left unreacted which had physical properties unlike those of any known gas. It proved to be a new element. Because of its complete lack of reactivity, the new gas was named "argon," which is Greek for "the lazy one."

The other inert gases were discovered by Ramsay and H. W. Travers soon thereafter, except for radon, which is the product of the radioactive decay of radium and, of course, was not discovered until after the isolation of substantial amounts of radium had been accomplished. Radon itself is a radioactive gas and decays within a matter of days to form another radioactive element, polonium.

The molecules of the inert gases were found to be monatomic; that is, they consist of single atoms. This shows that the atoms of the inert gases fail to form compounds not only with the atoms of other elements, but also with atoms of their own kind.

The discovery of the inert gases had far-reaching effects on chemical theory. Since the atoms of the inert gases are utterly unreactive, it must be concluded that they are very stable in the uncombined state. In fact, the atoms are so stable that they have nothing to "gain" in the way of additional stability by combining with other atoms, and thus remain forever uncombined. By studying their electronic structure, we may hope to discover a clue as to the type of electronic structure which other, less stable, atoms acquire when they combine to form compounds.

Hydrogen

The element hydrogen enjoys a unique status among the elements. Some of its reactions resemble those of the alkali metals, and others resemble those of the halogens. For example, hydrogen reacts with chlorine to form hydrogen chloride (HCl, compare with NaCl) and with sulfur to form hydrogen sulfide (H_2S, compare with Na_2S). But hydrogen reacts also with sodium to form sodium hydride (NaH, compare with NaCl) and with calcium to form calcium hydride (CaH_2, compare with $CaCl_2$). Some of the physical properties of hydrogen are as follows:

Atomic number:	1	Melting point:	$-259°C$
Atomic weight:	1.008	Boiling point:	$-252.7°C$

At room temperature, hydrogen is a colorless and odorless gas. Hydrogen was first distinguished from other gases by Henry Cavendish around 1770.

The Periodic Chart of the Elements

In Dalton's atomic theory, the most important property which distinguishes the atoms of one element from those of another is the atomic weight. Early in the development of chemistry, attempts were therefore made to find regular relationships between the atomic weights of the elements and their chemical properties. The pioneer in this field was the German chemist, J. W. Döbereiner, who made notable progress as early as 1820. However, the reader will recall that at that time the atomic weight scale had not yet been firmly settled, and that only relatively few of the elements were known. Chemists of the time were busy debating atomic theory and laying the foundations of organic chemistry—the chemistry of carbon compounds. They were not ready to move on this "front" as well.

Forty years later, after the question of the atomic weight scale had been solved and many new elements had been discovered, the time was ripe for a new search for relationships between atomic weights and chemical properties. Many celebrated chemists participated in this search, notably J. A. R. Newlands of Britain and Lothar Meyer of Germany. Yet the major credit for the final result of their efforts—the periodic chart of the elements—belongs to the Russian chemist, Dimitri I. Mendeleev.

After the scientific revolution at the beginning of the twentieth century, it was realized that the distinguishing property of each element is not its atomic weight, but its nuclear charge, expressed conveniently by means of the atomic number (see Chapter 8). It is therefore logical to try to relate the chemical properties of the elements to their atomic number. Atomic numbers were not available to Mendeleev, however, who therefore used atomic weights. His results, nevertheless, are in substantial agreement with the results one obtains using atomic numbers.

As a first step, let us list the elements in order of increasing atomic number, as shown in the table.

Symbol	H	He	Li	Be	B	C	N	O	F	Ne	Na	Mg
Atomic No.	1	2	3	4	5	6	7	8	9	10	11	12

Symbol	Al	Si	P	S	Cl	Ar	K	Ca	Sc	Ti	V	Cr
Atomic No.	13	14	15	16	17	18	19	20	21	22	23	24

Symbol	Mn	Fe	Co	Ni	Cu	Zn	Ga	Ge	As	Se	Br	Kr
Atomic No.	25	26	27	28	29	30	31	32	33	34	35	36

Symbol	Rb	Sr
Atomic No.	37	38

In order to emphasize the point that we want to make, certain of the elements have been placed in boxes. In the first box we find the element

Dimitri Ivanovitch Mendeleev:
1834–1907

Mendeleev's periodic chart, published in 1869, systematized knowledge of the properties of the elements and predicted the existence of several then undiscovered elements.

helium, followed by an alkali metal and an alkaline earth metal. In the second and in each of the other boxes we find first a halogen, then an inert gas, then an alkali metal, and then an alkaline earth metal. The sequence is always in that order. In other words, if we begin with any member of the halogen family, regardless of its atomic number, then the element of next higher atomic number is always an inert gas, the second one an alkali metal, and the third one an alkaline earth metal. Thus, there is an orderly relationship between the atomic numbers and the family characteristics of the elements. This orderliness is shown best by means of the periodic chart of the elements, in Figure 10-1.

The periodic chart arranges the elements in several rows or "periods" such that each row begins with an alkali metal and ends with an inert gas. The chart therefore places all of the alkali metals into the single vertical column labeled "I" in Figure 10-1, and all of the inert gases appear in the single column labeled "VIII." In this way one achieves the remarkable result that all elements appearing in the same column are members of one and the same family. For example, column II lists all the alkaline earth metals, and column VII all the halogens. The elements shown in the other columns have not yet been discussed in detail, but here again each column contains all the elements belonging to that particular family. For example, in column III there is a strong family resemblance between boron (B) and aluminum (Al), as shown by the similar molecular formulas of some of their compounds, such as $AlCl_3$ and BCl_3, or $LiBH_4$ and $LiAlH_4$.

121

Metalloids and Non-metals

Transition Metals

I	II											III	IV	V	VI	VII	VIII
1 H Hydrogen																	2 He Helium
3 Li Lithium	4 Be Beryllium											5 B Boron	6 C Carbon	7 N Nitrogen	8 O Oxygen	9 F Fluorine	10 Ne Neon
11 Na Sodium	12 Mg Magnesium											13 Al Aluminum	14 Si Silicon	15 P Phosphorus	16 S Sulfur	17 Cl Chlorine	18 Ar Argon
19 K Potassium	20 Ca Calcium	21 Sc Scandium	22 Ti Titanium	23 V Vanadium	24 Cr Chromium	25 Mn Manganese	26 Fe Iron	27 Co Cobalt	28 Ni Nickel	29 Cu Copper	30 Zn Zinc	31 Ga Gallium	32 Ge Germanium	33 As Arsenic	34 Se Selenium	35 Br Bromine	36 Kr Krypton
37 Rb Rubidium	38 Sr Strontium	39 Y Yttrium	40 Zr Zirconium	41 Nb Niobium	42 Mo Molybdenum	43 Tc Technetium	44 Ru Ruthenium	45 Rh Rhodium	46 Pd Palladium	47 Ag Silver	48 Cd Cadmium	49 In Indium	50 Sn Tin	51 Sb Antimony	52 Te Tellurium	53 I Iodine	54 Xe Xenon
55 Cs Cesium	56 Ba Barium	57 La Lanthanum	72 Hf Hafnium	73 Ta Tantalum	74 W Tungsten	75 Re Rhenium	76 Os Osmium	77 Ir Iridium	78 Pt Platinum	79 Au Gold	80 Hg Mercury	81 Tl Thallium	82 Pb Lead	83 Bi Bismuth	84 Po Polonium	85 At Astatine	86 Rn Radon
87 Fr Francium	88 Ra Radium	89 Ac Actinium														70 Yb Ytterbium	71 Lu Lutetium

Lanthanides (Rare Earth Metals)

58 Ce Cerium	59 Pr Praseodymium	60 Nd Neodymium	61 Pm Promethium	62 Sm Samarium	63 Eu Europium	64 Gd Gadolinium	65 Tb Terbium	66 Dy Dysprosium	67 Ho Holmium	68 Er Erbium	69 Tm Thulium

Actinides

90 Th Thorium	91 Pa Protoactinium	92 U Uranium	93 Np Neptunium	94 Pu Plutonium	95 Am Americium	96 Cm Curium	97 Bk Berkelium	98 Cf Californium	99 Es Einsteinium	100 Fm Fermium	101 Md Mendelevium	102 No Nobelium

Fig. 10-1. Periodic chart of the elements.

A number of columns appear under the single heading "Transition Metals." This group of elements includes some of the best-known metals of our civilization, such as iron, copper, zinc, nickel, and silver. Here again each column corresponds to a family, but the transition elements are enough alike so that it is convenient to talk about them as if they were a single large family.

Closer examination of the periodic chart shows that there is an irregularity beginning with element 58 and ending with element 71, and also beginning with element 90 and continuing to the end of the chart. While elements 57 and 89 resemble 21 and 39, element 58 is *not* a member of the same family as 22 and 40, element 59 is *not* a member of the same family as 23 and 41, and so on. It is not until we come to element 72 that we have again a member of the family to which 22 and 40 belong. Elements 58 through 71 are almost identical chemically and therefore form a family all by themselves. This is the family of the lanthanides or *rare-earth metals,* so named because of their rare occurrence in nature. Similarly, the elements beginning with element 90 and continuing to the end of the chart form a separate family, called the *actinide* family. Since these elements form separate families, they have been placed in a separate portion of the chart.

A dividing line has been drawn in the periodic chart to separate the metals from the nonmetals. Actually, the distinction between metals and nonmetals is not always clear-cut, and some of the elements bordering on the dividing line have properties that are intermediate between those of metals and nonmetals. For example, the electrical conductivity of the borderline element germanium is a thousand times smaller than that of tin, a more typical metal, but it is enormously larger than that of white phosphorous, a typical nonmetal.

Uses of the Periodic Chart

In 1889, D. I. Mendeleev was guest of honor of the Chemical Society of London in recognition of his work on the formulation and use of the periodic chart. The address he delivered at that time is a beautiful summary of the various uses to which the periodic chart can be put.* We shall describe some of these uses in this section. In order to gain the correct historical perspective, we must bear in mind that 1889 was still in the era of

---

* D. I. Mendeleev, *Journal of the Chemical Society* (London), **55**, 634–656 (1889).

Dalton's unstructured atom; atomic numbers were still unknown, and several elements were as yet undiscovered. The periodic chart of Mendeleev was obtained by listing the elements in order of increasing atomic weight, and since the atomic weight usually increases as the atomic number increases, his chart was essentially the same as Figure 10-1.

Perhaps the most important feature of the periodic chart is that all the elements belonging to a given family are listed in a single column, and the similarities of their chemical reactions are thereby emphasized. Thus, new reactions and the molecular formulas of new compounds may readily be predicted from the analogy to known facts about the other members of the same family.

However, there are also some striking regularities among the elements in any one period or row. For example, the following regularities have been noted for the series of elements silver (Ag), cadmium (Cd), indium (In), tin (Sn), antimony (Sb), tellurium (Te) and iodine (I), which occupy adjacent positions in the fifth row. Note the regular decrease in density, the regular increase in "oxidation number":

Element	Ag	Cd	In	Sn	Sb	Te	I
Density of pure element...	10.5	8.6	7.4	7.2	6.7	6.4	4.9
Formula of oxide*.......	Ag_2O	Cd_2O_2	In_2O_3	Sn_2O_4	Sb_2O_5	Te_2O_6	I_2O_7

* Formula as written by Mendeleev, to emphasize the regular increase in the quantity of oxygen in the series.

Perhaps the most important use of the periodic chart was to pinpoint the as-yet-undiscovered elements. Before the formulation of the chart, there was no special reason to expect the discovery of new elements, and the new ones which were discovered from time to time appeared to be possessed of quite novel properties. The periodic chart changed all that. For example, in 1871 no elements were known whose properties would fit the properties to be expected for the two elements between zinc (Zn) and arsenic (As) in the fourth row of the periodic chart. Mendeleev therefore concluded that these elements had not yet been discovered and left two empty spaces in the chart. He even went so far as to predict the properties of the elements that would eventually occupy these spaces, solely on the basis of the properties of the other, known elements in the same column or row. Within less than two decades both elements had been discovered, and Mendeleev lived to see his predictions confirmed with uncanny accuracy. For example, the predicted and actual properties of the element germanium (discovered by the German chemist, C. A. Winkler, in 1886) are shown below:

Property of germanium	Value predicted by Mendeleev	Actual value
Atomic weight............................	72	72.3
Density of element.......................	5.5	5.36
Formula of the oxide.....................	GeO_2	GeO_2
Density of the oxide.....................	4.7	4.70
Formula and properties of the chloride.........................	$GeCl_4$, boiling point a little under 100°C, density 1.9	$GeCl_4$, boiling point 83°C, density 1.88

Another use of the periodic chart was to indicate possible errors in the reported properties of known elements. For example, the element beryllium, whose chemistry was known only incompletely in 1871, had tentatively been assigned to the boron family. But Mendeleev realized that there was no room for another element of low molecular weight in column III, while there was an empty space right at the head of column II. He therefore concluded that beryllium must be an alkaline earth element, and later research has fully confirmed this view.

Is the periodic chart complete?

The various horizontal rows (periods) of the periodic chart differ in the number of elements that each contains. The first row consists of two elements, the next two rows of eight elements each, the fourth and fifth of eighteen elements each, and the sixth of thirty-two elements. The seventh row contains sixteen elements and is presumed to be incomplete.

Since the number of the elements in each of the rows will be an important clue in the explanation of the chart, we must ask ourselves whether we can be sure that these numbers are right. In other words, are we safe in assuming that all the elements which properly belong in the first six rows have by now been discovered? The answer to this question is decidedly "yes," and for the following reason: the atomic number of an element is equal to the number of electrons in the neutral atom. Since there is no such thing as half an electron or a fraction of an electron, the atomic number must always be a whole number. We can therefore be sure that we know all the elements in a given row if we can list an element for each whole number. For example, in the third row there is a large empty space between magnesium and aluminum, and we might wonder whether any undiscovered elements should go in there. But since the atomic number of magnesium is twelve and that of aluminum is thirteen, we can safely say that the space between magnesium and aluminum should be left empty.

*   *   *

We have now examined a substantial body of experimental data and its organization by means of the periodic chart. This organization strongly implies that there is a corresponding regularity in the submicroscopic structure of the atoms. In the next chapter, we shall inquire whether an extension of Bohr's model of the hydrogen atom can explain this regularity.

Suggestions for Further Reading

W. A. Tilden, "Mendeleev Memorial Lecture," *Journal of the Chemical Society* (London), **95,** 2077 (1909).

R. K. Duncan, *The New Knowledge* (London: Hodder & Stoughton, Ltd., 1909).

J. V. Quagliano, *Chemistry* (Englewood Cliffs, N. J.: Prentice-Hall, Inc., 1958) chap. 12.

L. Pauling, *College Chemistry* (San Francisco: W. H. Freeman & Company, 1950) chaps. 5, 9.

Besides ministering to our comfort, science also serves to satisfy certain needs of the human spirit. It helps us to understand the world and to feel at home in it. We are distressed by disorder, and always try to arrange in order the things with which we have to deal, whether they are the affairs of a nation, the books in a library, or our own ideas. Science satisfies us because it shows us that, behind the transient and confused pageant of nature, there is a permanent and orderly reality.

Angus Armitage (1947)

11 *The Structure of Atoms: III. Atoms with more than one Electron*

WE HAVE seen that when the elements are arranged in order of increasing atomic number, a striking harmony becomes apparent. At definite intervals there appear elements with closely related chemical properties. This permits the organization of the many elements into "families" and the construction of a periodic chart.

Whenever we have encountered a striking macroscopic simplicity or orderliness like this, we have sought for some submicroscopic orderliness to account for it. The situation is the same here. In the present case, it seems reasonable to assume that this periodicity is associated with the electronic structure of the atoms of each element. That is, repeating chemical properties are simply a reflection of repeating electronic structure.

Let us begin our discussion of electronic structure by reviewing the structure of the atoms beyond hydrogen, as deduced from the experiments of Rutherford. The nuclear charge of each element increases by one unit over that of the preceding element, and since each atom is electrically neutral, the number of electrons must also increase by one. Thus, helium has a nuclear charge of two and two electrons; lithium has a nuclear charge of three and three electrons; and so forth right through the periodic chart, to element number 102 which has a nuclear charge of 102 and 102 electrons.

Now, how are these electrons distributed about the nucleus? The great success of the Bohr theory in explaining the properties of the hydrogen atom suggests that the electrons may be circling around the nucleus in specific orbits, just as is the single electron of the hydrogen atom. Furthermore, we might suppose that the orbits are "quantized" in much the same fashion as for the hydrogen atom. If so, in which of the many possible orbits of the atom do the electrons reside? Are they all in one orbit, does each electron occupy a separate orbit, or is the distribution more complicated?

Refinements of the Bohr Theory

Before we can pursue this problem further, it is necessary to consider some of the refinements that have been made in the original Bohr model of the hydrogen atom. It is only on the basis of these refinements that a satisfactory theory of a "many electron" atom can be developed.

Additional orbits

In the normal hydrogen atom the electron occupies the orbit of lowest energy ($n = 1$). It will be recalled, however, that by the absorption of energy this electron can be "excited" to any of the orbits of higher quantum number. Thus, by studying the properties of the excited atom, we can learn about the nature of the orbits of quantum number greater than one.

First of all, it has been found that while there is only one orbit corresponding to the first quantum number, there can be several orbits, all of identical energy, for higher quantum numbers. Thus, for $n = 2$, there were found to be four orbits of equivalent energy, and for $n = 3$, nine orbits of identical energy. In general, there are n^2 orbits for the nth quantum number.

Three-dimensional orbitals

It was soon realized that the flat or planar model of the atom envisioned by Bohr was unrealistic, and that in all probability the atom was three-dimensional in extent. Even more important was the realization that it is impossible to locate exactly the position of a single electron at any given moment. In the macroscopic world the laws of mechanics permit us to give with exactness the past or future position of a moving body (the earth, for example), if we know its present position, the velocity with which it is moving, and the forces that are acting upon it. The same thing cannot be said for an object as small as an electron. Owing to the tiny size of the electron, the "light" that we must use to "see" the electron has enough energy to cause the electron to move out of its path. Thus, every time we try to locate the electron, the very act of "looking" causes it to change position and velocity. This disturbance obviously makes it impossible to give the exact position of the electron. All one can talk about is the region of space in which the probability of finding the electron is greatest.

This inability to obtain precise locations and velocities is called the *uncertainty principle*. It immediately rules out the definite orbits of Bohr, since they assign a definite location and velocity to each electron. In order to get around this difficulty, the three-dimensional *orbital* was invented. An orbital represents a region in space, surrounding the nucleus, in which one is most likely to find an electron with a given quantum number. The relationship between the now obsolete orbits of the Bohr model for the hydrogen atom and the corresponding three-dimensional orbitals becomes clear when we examine Figure 11-1. Each dot is a picture of the position of the electron at some particular instant. If many of these instantaneous pictures are superimposed, diagrams such as those shown on the right in the figure are obtained. The heavier the concentration of dots, the higher is the probability that the electron is in that region at any given instant. Note that the dots thin out gradually at the edge of the orbital, rather than ending abruptly.

It is of interest to consider further the shapes of these orbitals. By "shape" we mean a figure which is drawn so that there is a 95% probability of finding the electron within it. Some of these shapes are shown in Figure 11-2. Thus, an electron in the lowest energy state of the hydrogen atom with quantum number one will most probably be found in a spherical region called the 1s orbital. If the electron is excited to the second energy level, it may be found within a larger sphere (2s orbital), or in one of three 2p orbitals which extend symmetrically in two directions. If the electron is

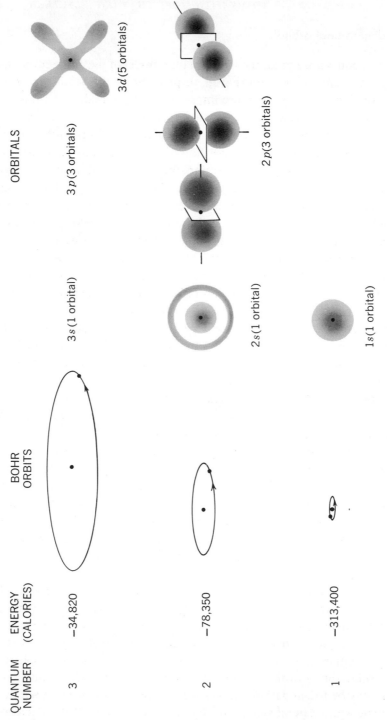

Fig. 11-1. Relationship of Bohr orbits to three-dimensional orbitals for the hydrogen atom.

raised to the third energy level, it may again be found in a spherical orbital (3s orbital), in one of three orbitals extending symmetrically in two directions (3p orbitals), or in one of five 3d orbitals extending in four directions. Excitation to still higher energy levels will find the electron in other orbitals of increasing complexity. It must be understood, of course, that the electron can occupy only one orbital at a time.

The letter designations s, p, d, and so forth, arose historically and are purely arbitrary. An s orbital is always spherical in symmetry, a p orbital extends symmetrically in two directions, and a d orbital extends in four directions. A group of orbitals, all having the same main quantum number, is referred to as a "shell of orbitals" or simply a "shell." As we have seen, the first shell ($n = 1$) consists of one orbital. The second shell ($n = 2$) consists of four orbitals: one 2s orbital and three 2p orbitals. The third shell consists of nine orbitals: one 3s, three 3p, and five 3d orbitals. The fourth shell consists of sixteen orbitals: one 4s, three 4p, five 4d, and seven additional orbitals which are designated as 4f. Note that the total number of orbitals in a shell is equal to n^2, where n is the quantum number of that shell.

Electron spin

At about the same time (1925) that the detailed picture of the orbitals of the hydrogen atom was worked out, two Dutch physicists, G. E. Uhlenbeck and S. Goudsmit, suggested that the finest details of the properties of the hydrogen atom could be explained if it was further assumed that the electron is spinning on its axis. According to their theory, all electrons are spinning at the same rate. However, the spin may be either in a clockwise direction or in a counterclockwise direction.

Atoms More Complex than the Hydrogen Atom

When dealing with atoms containing more than one electron, it is useful to assume that, to a first approximation, the orbitals in which the electrons reside are very much like those of the hydrogen atom. In particular, the orbitals may be grouped into shells, the energy of which increases with increasing quantum number. Again there is one orbital in the first shell, four in the second shell, nine in the third, and n^2 in the nth shell.

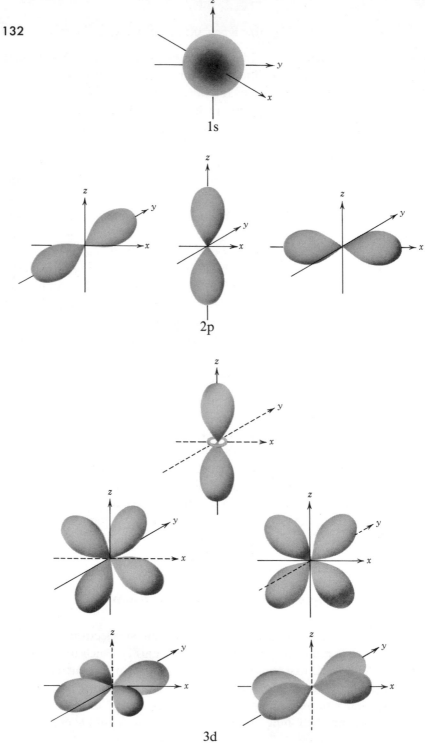

Fig. 11-2. Orbital shapes for the hydrogen atom. (After E. Cart-mell and G. W. A. Fowles, *Valency and Molecular Structure* (N. Y., Academic Press, 1956.)

The exclusion principle

When there is more than one electron in the atom, another problem comes up which did not exist for the hydrogen atom. How many electrons can each orbital accommodate? According to the German physicist, Wolfgang Pauli, the answer is very simple: there can be no more than two electrons in any orbital, and these electrons must be spinning on their axes in opposite directions. This concept is known as the *exclusion principle.*

Combined with the shell model of orbital structure, the exclusion principle leads to a picture of electronic structure bearing a strong relationship to the lengths of the periods in the periodic chart. Thus, there will be a maximum of two electrons in the first shell, eight in the second shell, eighteen in the third shell, and so forth. The numbers 2 and 8 correspond exactly to the lengths of the first two periods. This suggests that the filling of these shells coincides with the completion of a period. On the other hand, the third period, which consists of eight elements, is complete before the third shell, which can hold eighteen electrons, is filled. In order to explain this and other deviations, it is necessary to modify our basic assumption. Apparently the orbitals of more complex atoms have more complex energy relationships than those of the hydrogen atom.

Energy of orbitals in more complex atoms

In the helium atom, which has two electrons, both electrons are found in the 1s orbital. The next higher element, lithium, has three electrons. Two of these are found in the 1s orbital; but since this orbital is now full, the third electron must occupy one of the four orbitals of the second shell. Experiment has shown that it is always found in the 2s orbital.

Why does the third electron in lithium always occupy the 2s orbital instead of one of the three 2p orbitals? If the four orbitals were of equal energy, as they are in hydrogen, the third electron would occupy any one of the four orbitals in the second shell with equal probability. Evidently the energy of the 2s orbital in the lithium atom must be lower than that of the 2p orbitals.

When there is more than one electron in the atom, the electrons repel one another in addition to being attracted by the nucleus. These repulsions will have the effect of causing the *p* orbitals to be of higher energy than the *s* orbital of the same shell. In the same fashion, if the shell contains *d* orbitals, their energy will be higher than that of the *p* orbitals in the same shell; and the energy of the *f* orbitals will be higher than that of the *d* orbitals.

Using boxes to represent the various two-electron orbitals, these energy relations can be depicted for some of the simpler atoms, as in Figure 11-3. Dots are used to denote the electrons, and orbitals belonging to the same shell are connected by solid lines.

As the number of electrons becomes greater and greater, the differences in the energy of the *s, p, d,* and *f* orbitals in the same shell become greater also. Thus, for example, the difference in the energy between the 2*s* and the 2*p* orbitals is greater in lithium than in helium, as can be seen from Figure 11-3. These differences become so great that by the time we come to the 19-electron atom, potassium, the energy of the 4*s* orbital is lower

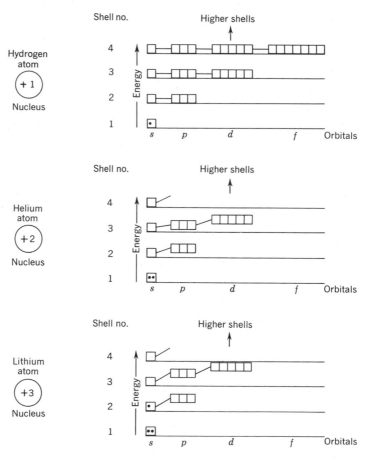

Fig. 11-3. Some orbital relationships. Note the increasing separation of the *s, p, d, . . .* orbitals in any given shell with increasing number of electrons. For convenience, the energy spacing of the shells has been depicted as uniform.

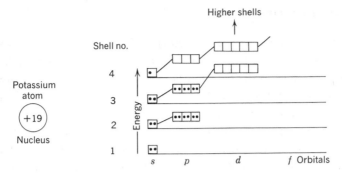

Fig. 11-4. Schematic representation of orbitals in the potassium atom.

than that of the 3d orbitals. This is just the reverse of what might have been expected on the basis of the simple hydrogen-like shell model. The energy relationships for the potassium atom are depicted in Figure 11-4.

The foregoing discussion may be summarized by the following set of rules which may be used to deduce the electronic structure of atoms. Each orbital can hold two electrons. As electrons are placed in orbitals, each electron goes into the next unfilled orbital with the lowest energy. For atoms of low atomic number, the energy relationship of the orbitals is similar to that of the hydrogen atom, except that in any one shell an s orbital is lower in energy than a p orbital, which in turn is lower than a d orbital. For atoms of higher atomic number, with many electrons, the energy relationships of the orbitals deviate more and more from those predicted on the basis of the hydrogen atom, and in fact, the electronic structure is determinable only by experiment.

Electronic Structure and the Periodic Chart

We are now ready to give an explanation of the periodicity in chemical properties of the elements in terms of electronic structure. For this purpose, it is convenient to divide the elements into two classes.

1. *The main-group elements.* These are the elements of the families that begin with H, Be, B, C, N, O, F, and He, respectively. The main-group elements are listed in columns I–VIII of the periodic chart on page 122.
2. *The subgroup elements.* These are the transition metals, the rare earths, and the actinides.

The main-group elements

Alkali metals. It has been noted that lithium has two electrons in the first shell and one electron in the second shell. For the next alkali metal, sodium, the electron distribution is as shown in Figure 11-5. We see that in sodium we again have a structure with just one electron in the outermost shell, although this time it is the third shell.

On examining the electronic structures of the other alkali metals, it is found that in every case there is one electron in the outermost shell. Potassium, for example, has one electron in the fourth shell, as shown in Figure 11-4. This is again the outermost shell. As stated before, the nineteenth electron goes into the $4s$ orbital rather than the $3d$ orbital, because the former is of lower energy.

The fact that each alkali metal atom has one electron in the outermost shell is very striking indeed. Here is the underlying orderliness that can account for the similarity in chemical properties: here is a group of elements, all belonging to the same family, with electronic structures closely related to one another. This observation suggests a possible generalization:

The number of electrons in the outer shell of orbitals is the same for all members of a given family.

Alkaline earth metals. Let us see whether this generalization applies to the members of the alkaline earth family as well. The electronic structures of elements 4, 12, and 20 are depicted in Figure 11-6. In this case we find two electrons in the outermost shell of orbitals. Evidently the generalization again applies.

A similar situation exists for all of the main-group families discussed in the preceding chapter. All members of a given family have the same number of electrons in the outermost shell of orbitals. Furthermore, this

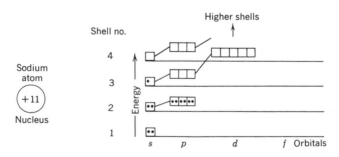

Fig. 11-5. Schematic representation of orbitals in the sodium atom.

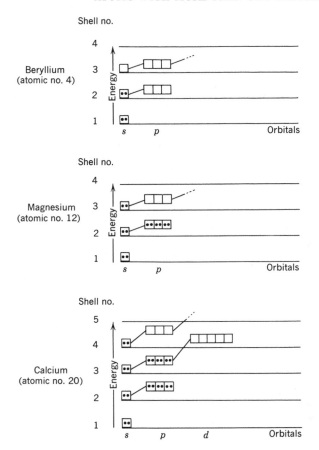

Fig. 11-6. Schematic representation of the orbitals in atoms of the alkaline earth metals.

number of electrons is equal to the group number of the family, that is, the Roman numeral at the head of the column in the periodic chart. Thus, group I consists of the alkali metals, all of which have one electron in the outer shell. The alkaline earths constitute group II, and these elements have two electrons in the outer shell. The halogens are members of group VII, and we would therefore expect these elements to have seven electrons in their outermost shell. This is indeed the case.

The subgroup elements

The series of metals beginning with scandium (21) and ending with zinc (30) belong to the family of transition metals and are typical of that family. The element immediately preceding scandium in the periodic chart is calcium, whose electronic structure is shown in Figure 11-6. Here the outermost electrons are in the 4s orbital rather than in the still vacant 3d orbitals. In the series beginning with scandium, these 3d orbitals fill up.

It is the filling of these inner orbitals that leads to the special chemical properties of these subgroup elements. Thus, scandium has one electron in the 3d orbitals, titanium two, vanadium three, and so on, until a total of ten electrons has been added, filling the 3d orbitals and consequently the third shell. This latter condition occurs with zinc, which has a total of 30 electrons. Examples of these electronic structures are shown in Figure 11-7.

The element immediately following zinc is gallium (31). In this element, the thirty-first electron goes into the vacant 4p orbital, leading to the electronic structure shown in Figure 11-7. The structure of gallium is therefore like that of aluminum, with three electrons in the outermost shell of orbitals. Gallium thus belongs to group III of the main-group elements.

What has been illustrated here is true for all subgroup elements. Each element differs from the one preceding it in the periodic chart by one electron. For the subgroup elements, this electron occupies an empty orbital of an inner shell rather than an orbital of the outermost shell.

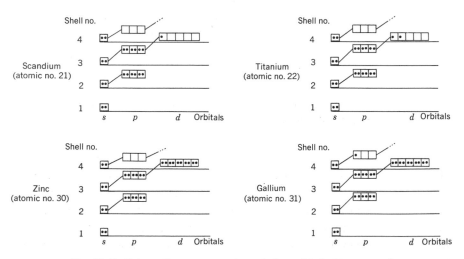

Fig. 11-7. Schematic representation of the orbitals in atoms of some transition elements and gallium.

The octet rule

The family of elements called the inert gases deserves special consideration. The electronic structures of the first four are shown in Figure 11-8.

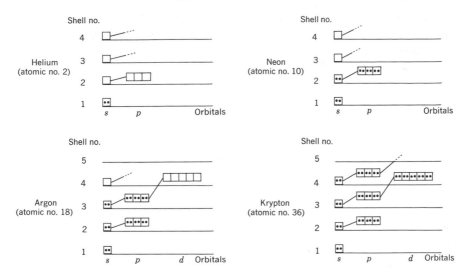

Fig. 11-8. Schematic representation of the orbitals in some inert gas atoms.

In every case, with the exception of helium, the outer shell of orbitals contains eight electrons. There must be something peculiarly stable about an octet of electrons in the outermost shell, since we have seen that the inert gases are all completely unreactive. Helium is an exception to this rule of eight. However, the first shell cannot hold more than two electrons. Evidently, the filling of this shell also leads to a stable condition even though the shell contains only two electrons.

In 1916 the American chemist, G. N. Lewis, suggested that atoms other than those of the inert gases would also be more stable if they could some-

Gilbert Newton Lewis: 1875–1946

Among Lewis' many contributions are the rule of the octet and theories of ionic and covalent bonding.

how acquire eight electrons in the outermost shell of orbitals. We shall see in the next chapters that this is a very powerful concept when we come to consider the problem of chemical reactivity and compound formation.

Suggestions for Further Reading

E. W. Müller, "Atoms Visualized," *Scientific American,* June 1957, p. 113.

G. Gamow, "The Principle of Uncertainty," *Scientific American,* Jan. 1958, p. 51.

J. J. G. McCue, *The World of Atoms* (New York: Ronald Press Co., 1956) chap. 53.

B. Hoffmann, *The Strange Story of the Quantum* (New York: Harper and Brothers, Publishers, 1947).

F. Winsor, *The Space Child's Mother Goose* (New York: Simon & Schuster, 1958).

Thoughts are but dreams till their effects be tried.

William Shakespeare

12 *Principles of Compound Formation: I. Ionic Compounds*

How DO atoms combine to form molecules? Now that we have studied the electron orbitals in the atom, we are ready to consider this question. In this and the next chapter we shall study the nature of the chemical bond. We shall limit our considerations to the eight main families of elements, which are listed in columns I–VIII of the periodic chart on page 122. However, similar concepts of interatomic binding apply also to the transition metals, the rare-earth metals, and the actinide metals.

141

Two Basic Assumptions

The discussion of the principles of compound formation will be based on the following assumptions.

1. *The electrons in the outermost shell of an atom are the only ones that need to be considered in any theory of compound formation.*

We have seen that all members of the same family of elements have an identical number of electrons in the outermost shell. This number is the one conspicuous feature of electronic structure that is uniquely characteristic of each family. Since chemical properties are also characteristic of each family, it seems plausible to assume a close relationship between chemical properties and outer electrons.

This argument becomes even more convincing when we study the electrons which are *not* in the outermost shell. The distribution of these inner electrons among their shells is identical with that of an inert gas. We may therefore assume that these electrons are inert, leaving only the electrons in the outermost shell to determine chemical reactivity and the formation of molecules.

2. *Molecules are generally formed only if each atom acquires a highly stable electron configuration in the process. The most stable electron configuration for any atom is one which is like that of an inert gas.*

We shall see that there are two processes by which each atom in the molecule can acquire such a stable electron configuration: by electron transfer, and by electron sharing. Both of these processes of compound formation will be discussed in detail. In this chapter we shall consider electron transfer, which results in the formation of ionic compounds.

The Formation of Ions by Electron Transfer

Let us first consider the lithium atom (atomic number 3), which has the electron configuration:

The shells higher than the second are empty and are not shown. Note that the first shell is filled, while the second shell contains but one electron. Now let us compare this electron configuration with that of an atom of helium (atomic number 2), the nearest inert gas:

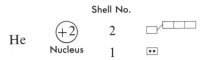

The two configurations differ only by the additional electron in the second shell of the lithium atom. The loss of this electron by the lithium atom would result in the formation of a lithium ion which has an electron configuration identical to that of the inert and stable helium atom, except that the lithium ion has a net charge of $+1$:

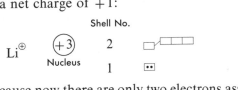

The charge is $+1$ because now there are only two electrons associated with the nucleus, which has a charge of $+3$.

Next let us consider the element fluorine. Here the electron configuration is as follows:

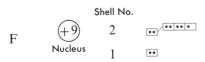

The shells higher than the second are empty and are again omitted. In order to see how the fluorine atom might acquire a more stable electron configuration, let us consider the inert gas nearest to fluorine, neon:

The neon atom has eight electrons in the second shell, whereas the fluorine atom has only seven. Fluorine should therefore be stabilized by the gain of an electron to complete the octet in the second shell. This would lead to the formation of a fluoride* ion with a net charge of -1.

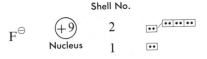

* When an atom gains electrons to become a negative ion, the ending of the name is changed to *-ide*.

Under what circumstances will a lithium atom lose an electron, and a fluorine atom gain one? One theory of compound formation is this: when lithium is brought into contact with fluorine, the lithium atoms transfer their outer electron to the fluorine atoms, to produce lithium ions (Li^+) and fluoride ions (F^-). The ions are then held together by the electrostatic attraction of their opposite charges, forming "molecules" of lithium fluoride. The reaction proceeds readily because in the process, both the lithium and the fluorine atoms achieve stable configurations like the inert gases.

Since each lithium atom *loses* one electron and each fluorine atom *requires* one electron, we anticipate that lithium fluoride will have the formula LiF; that is, for each lithium atom there will be one fluorine atom. This prediction is fully in agreement with experiment.

The preceding theory of compound formation may be summarized as follows:

There is a transfer of electrons from the atoms of one element to those of the other to produce ions with electron configurations like those of inert gases; the ions are then held together by the electrostatic attraction of their opposite charges.

The same theory should apply also in cases other than lithium fluoride, but it will be convenient first to simplify our rather cumbersome method of representing electron configurations.

Symbolic Representation of Atoms and Ions

Since we seek a simple representation, we shall depict only those characteristics that are useful in our discussion of chemical bonding.

We saw in Chapter 11 that the chemical properties of the main-group elements depend on the number of electrons in the outermost shell. For the elements in columns I through VIII of the periodic chart (page 122), this number ranges from one to eight, and the electrons occupy as many as four orbitals. Thus, the essential electronic feature of the elements can be summarized by writing the symbol of the element, surrounded by four boxes representing four orbitals of the outermost shell. The electrons in these orbitals are represented by dots, as before. A number of examples follow:

Element	Electrons in outer shell	Symbolic representation of atom
Lithium...............................	1	▫ Li ▫
Fluorine..............................	7	⦂ F ▫
Oxygen...............................	6	▫ O ▫
Phosphorous..........................	5	▫ P ▫
Neon.................................	8	⦂ Ne ⦂
Calcium..............................	2	▫ Ca ▫
Chlorine.............................	7	⦂ Cl ▫

The reader will note that, in this representation, one electron is placed into each of the four orbitals before any of the electrons are paired up.

Since the first shell contains only one orbital, the elements hydrogen and helium, for which the first is the outer shell, are represented as follows:

$$\text{H} \;\square \qquad \text{He} \;\boxed{\cdot\cdot}$$

The same symbolism can be extended to atoms which have gained or lost electrons to become ions. Thus:

$$\boxed{\text{Na}} \cdot \xrightarrow{\;-e^{\ominus}\;} \boxed{\text{Na}}^{\oplus} \quad \text{or} \quad \text{Na}^{\oplus}$$

The symbol at the right is a simpler version for the sodium ion. Other examples are:

$$\text{H}\square \xrightarrow{\;-e^{\ominus}\;} \text{H}\square^{\oplus} \quad \text{or} \quad \text{H}^{\oplus}$$

$$\boxed{\text{F}} \cdot \xrightarrow{\;+e^{\ominus}\;} \boxed{\text{F}}^{\ominus} \quad \text{or} \quad \text{F}^{\ominus}$$

$$\boxed{\text{O}} \xrightarrow{\;+2e^{\ominus}\;} \boxed{\text{O}}^{\ominus} \quad \text{or} \quad \text{O}^{\ominus}$$

The plus and minus signs in these formulas indicate the number of electrons lost or gained.

Ionic Compounds

The crystalline compound formed by the interaction of lithium metal with gaseous fluorine is called an *ionic* compound because it is composed of lithium ions and fluoride ions, held together by the mutual attraction of positive and negative charges. If our theory is correct, we would predict the formation of numerous other ionic compounds by the process of electron transfer. For example, calcium has two electrons in its outermost shell, and we would anticipate that it would lose these to become a calcium ion (Ca^{++}) if some "electron acceptor" were available. The electronic configuration of the chlorine atom suggests that it should react with calcium metal, and indeed it does. Furthermore, since each calcium atom must lose *two* electrons, while each chlorine atom accepts only one, the theory would predict that the compound formed would contain *two* chlorine atoms for each calcium atom:

Chemical analysis of the reaction product shows the ratio of calcium to chlorine to be $CaCl_2$, as predicted.

When oxygen is brought into contact with calcium, the formation of an ionic compound is again anticipated, with an oxygen atom gaining the two electrons lost by each calcium atom.

Since the number of electrons lost by the calcium metal (per atom) is equal to the number gained by the oxygen, the predicted formula is CaO, which is in fact the experimentally determined one.

Numerous examples of this kind could be furnished to support the postulate that compound formation results from electron transfer. The atomic ratios in the compounds are then correctly predicted by considering the number of electrons lost or gained per atom in order to achieve an inert gas configuration. The outstanding and obvious characteristic of these ionic compounds is that they are composed of charged particles (positive and negative ions). This should give them characteristic properties capable of being detected experimentally.

Electrical Properties of Ionic Compounds

When current electricity was discovered in the period around 1800, many people turned their attention to the effects that electric currents might have on various substances. Most active in this field were Sir Humphry Davy, J. J. Berzelius, and Michael Faraday. Out of the experiments of these men developed the theory that the combination of elements to form compounds must somehow involve electrical charges. For example, Berzelius was one of the first to maintain that electric charges are responsible for compound formation. This idea is strikingly similar to our modern concept of ionic compounds, and it is interesting to note that it was formulated as early as 1815, long before our present-day ideas of atoms as consisting of electrically charged electrons and nuclei were even dreamed of. As a matter of fact, this was only a few years after Dalton's theory had been published, first postulating the *existence* of atoms.

Electrolysis

One of the most striking of the properties of ionic compounds is their behavior when electric currents are passed through them. If solid sodium chloride is placed in a suitable container and heated to around 800°C, the salt melts and becomes liquid. If now a pair of graphite electrodes is placed in the melt and connected to a battery, as shown in Figure 12-1, a series of events occurs which is invaluable in providing insight into the nature of ionic compounds. First of all, the molten salt conducts the current. This can be shown by inserting an electric lamp in the circuit: the lamp will glow, indicating that the current is flowing. On the other hand, if the salt is allowed to solidify again the lamp will cease to glow, indicating that the current is no longer flowing. Thus, the simple process of converting salt from a liquid to a solid converts it from a conductor of electricity to a nonconductor.

Furthermore, while the current is flowing through the molten salt, things are happening at the electrodes which suggest that this flow of current must involve the ions of which the salt is assumed to be composed. At the negative electrode a silvery metal begins to deposit, while chlorine gas bubbles off at the positive electrode; in other words, the passage of the current is converting the sodium chloride to the elements from which it was formed. This behavior can be explained most readily by the assumption that molten sodium chloride consists of positively charged sodium

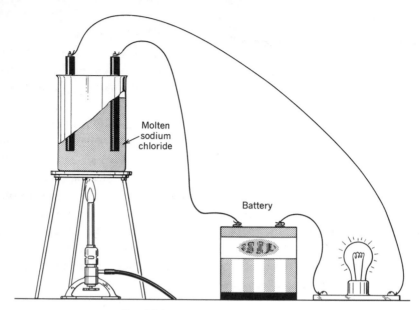

Fig. 12-1. Apparatus for electrolysis.

ions and negatively charged chloride ions which are free to move and are attracted to the electrode of opposite charge. That these ions exist *prior* to the melting process can be inferred from the fact that many other substances on melting do *not* conduct an electric current. Therefore the melting process itself does not create the ions; they must be present also in the solid sodium chloride. The solid does not conduct a current because the ions are not free to move.

In more detail, the positive sodium ions are attracted toward the negative electrode and the negative chloride ions are attracted toward the positive electrode, as shown in Figure 12-2. Each chloride ion that reaches the positive electrode deposits an electron there and becomes a neutral chlorine atom; each sodium ion that reaches the negative electrode picks up an electron and becomes a neutral sodium atom. Thus, the net result of these changes is, obviously, the transport of electrons from the negative electrode to the positive electrode. This ionic conductance must be contrasted with the passage of electricity through a wire, in which case the electrons themselves move.

The deposition and acquisition of electrons is responsible for the chemical changes that occur at the electrodes. Thus, as the chloride ion loses an electron to the positive electrode it becomes a neutral chlorine atom, and on its pairing up with another similarly formed chlorine atom there is formed a molecule of chlorine:

$$2 \; [\ddot{Cl}]^{\ominus} \longrightarrow 2 \; [\ddot{Cl}] \; + \; 2e^- \quad \text{(at the positive electrode)}$$

$$2 \; [\ddot{Cl}] \longrightarrow Cl_2 \quad \text{(chlorine gas)}$$

In a similar fashion, metallic sodium is formed from sodium ions:

$$[Na]^{\oplus} \; + \; e^- \longrightarrow [Na] \quad \text{(metallic sodium)}$$

The process of decomposing compounds by means of an electric current is called *electrolysis*. It has wide industrial applications: in the commercial production of sodium, chlorine, hydrogen, copper, aluminum, and many other substances; in all types of electroplating, such as silver-plating or chromium-plating; and in chemical analysis.

The "Molecular Weight" of Ionic Compounds

The reader may have noted that the term "molecule" was used earlier in this chapter to designate the unit produced by the interaction of a lithium ion with a fluoride ion (Li^+F^-), but that quotation marks were used to suggest that this was not an accurate use of the word. Strictly speaking, the term does not apply to ionic compounds. The reason for this will become

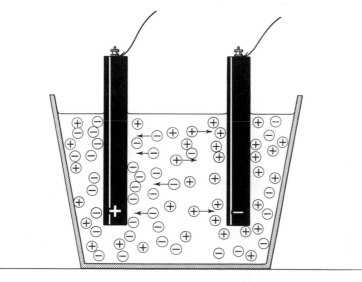

Fig. 12-2. Movement of ions during electrolysis.

clear when we consider the results of studies of the vapor of the ionic compound, sodium chloride, at temperatures around 1000°C. At these temperatures sodium chloride is vaporized to a measurable extent. When the molecular weight of the vapor is determined, one discovers that the vapor consists not only of molecules with the formula Na^+Cl^-, but also of molecules having the formulas

$$\begin{array}{lll}
Na^{\oplus}Cl^{\ominus} & & Na^{\oplus}Cl^{\ominus}Na^{\oplus} \\
Cl^{\ominus}Na^{\oplus} & \text{and} & Cl^{\ominus}Na^{\oplus}Cl^{\ominus}, \; \ldots \text{and so on.} \\
(Na_2Cl_2) & & (Na_3Cl_3)
\end{array}$$

In other words, while the *simplest* formula is NaCl, "molecules" with formulas that are integral multiples of this formula also exist, and we are unable to say which of these is the "true" formula of sodium chloride.

When we examine a solid crystal of sodium chloride—or of any other ionic compound, for that matter—the situation becomes even more complex, and we cannot possibly think in terms of "molecules" of sodium chloride. True enough, in the crystal there is one sodium ion for each chloride ion, but we cannot say definitely which chloride ion belongs to which sodium ion. The crystal is really a network or lattice of sodium ions and chloride ions, the whole being held together by electrostatic attractions. In this sense, then, the whole crystal is really a single giant molecule.

This situation can be understood if we look more carefully at the properties of electrically charged bodies such as ions. If we take a positively charged body and bring a negatively charged body into its vicinity, the two bodies are attracted to one another, but it *does not* matter from which direction the first body is approached. The electrostatic force extends equally in all directions, and its strength depends only on the distance separating the two bodies. Thus, the number of negatively charged ions that can be attracted to a single positively charged ion depends, in the first approximation, only on the space available around the positive ion. In the case of a sodium chloride crystal, each sodium ion is surrounded by six chloride ions and each chloride ion in turn is surrounded by six sodium ions. A tiny portion of a crystal of sodium chloride is shown diagrammatically in Figure 12-3.

There are other physical properties which indicate that compounds such as sodium chloride, calcium oxide, or silver bromide are ionic. For example, crystals of these substances are very difficult to vaporize. This indicates that the particles of which these crystals are composed are held together by very strong forces which are overcome only if considerable energy is supplied.

Fig. 12-3. Arrangement of ions in a sodium chloride crystal. From
J. Quagliano, *Chemistry*, 1958. p. 42. Courtesy Prentice-Hall, Inc.

Properties of Ionic Compounds in Solution

When an ionic compound is dissolved in water, the ions separate from
one another and behave in an essentially independent manner. Thus, solutions in water of lithium chloride (Li^+Cl^-), sodium chloride (Na^+Cl^-),
and potassium chloride (K^+Cl^-) display identical chemical reactions,
typical of the chloride ion, regardless of the nature of the positive ion. For
example, they react with silver fluoride (Ag^+F^-) to produce the insoluble
substance, silver chloride (Ag^+Cl^-). In each case the reaction which
takes place is that of silver ion with chloride ion:

$$Ag^{\oplus} (\text{from } Ag^{\oplus}F^{\ominus}) \quad + \quad Cl^{\ominus} (\text{from } Li^{\oplus}Cl^{\ominus}, Na^{\oplus}Cl^{\ominus}, \text{ or } K^{\oplus}Cl^{\ominus})$$
$$\longrightarrow AgCl \text{ (insoluble in water)}$$

Similarly, if a set of compounds contains a common positive ion, solutions
of these compounds will display reactions characteristic of the common
positive ion, regardless of the nature of the negative ions. For example,
solutions of calcium chloride ($CaCl_2$), calcium bromide ($CaBr_2$), and cal-

cium sulfide (CaS) all react with sodium carbonate (Na_2CO_3) to form insoluble calcium carbonate ($CaCO_3$).

There is much additional evidence for the view that ionic compounds dissociate into free ions in water solutions. For example, such solutions conduct electric current in much the same way as do the molten salts. The chemical reactions which occur at the electrodes again suggest that ions are being attracted to the electrodes.

To him who is a discoverer in the field (of science), the
products of his imagination appear so necessary and natural
that he regards them, and would like to have them regarded
by others, not as creations of thought but as given realities.

Albert Einstein (1934)

13 *Principles of Compound Formation: II. Covalent Compounds*

ALTHOUGH the theory of the ionic bond will explain the stability of many
known compounds, it cannot be the only explanation for molecule formation. This becomes clear as soon as we consider such molecules as H_2 or
Cl_2, which consist of two *identical* atoms. Since in these molecules the two
atoms have identical chemical properties, it is hard to see why one atom
should gain an electron and the other lose one, as must be the case if the
molecule is to consist of a pair of ions. Evidently some other mode of atomic
bonding must exist.

The Covalent Bond

Attempts at developing a theory of the nature of the chemical bond which does not involve the formation of ions began soon after J. J. Thomson's discovery of the electron. Although at this writing the theory is not yet complete, the basic ideas are well established. The most important of these ideas, which is due to G. N. Lewis, is that atoms may also achieve an inert gas electron configuration by the *sharing* of electrons, as well as by transfer.

To illustrate this idea, let us consider two isolated chlorine atoms moving slowly toward one another. As long as the atoms are separated by distances that are large compared to their own diameters, the electron orbitals of the two atoms are well apart. But as the atoms move closer and closer, electrical interactions become important, and the motion of the electrons in each atom is influenced by the nearness of the other atom. If we consider for a moment the approach of two *filled* orbitals, then we expect the negative charges of the electrons to exert a repulsion and prevent the two atoms from approaching closely.

Electrical repulsion
between two filled orbitals

But if each of the two orbitals holds only a single electron, then there is room for another electron in each.

The two orbitals can therefore overlap, thus bringing the electron of each atom closer to the positive charge of the nucleus of the other atom, and a net attraction can result.

Overlapping of two
half-filled orbitals

This, of course, is just another way of saying that a bond can be formed. As the atoms continue to approach and the orbitals overlap more and more, a state is eventually reached in which the two electrons must be regarded as moving in a single orbital, formed from the blending or combination of the two individual orbitals, and one can no longer tell which of the two electrons belongs to which atom.

$$:\overset{..}{\underset{..}{Cl}} \,\,\boxed{..}\,\, \overset{..}{\underset{..}{Cl}}:$$

Orbitals merge to form a single orbital
which is shared equally by both atoms

The shared orbital and electrons now belong equally to both atoms, and each atom thus acquires a stable *octet* of electrons.

It is a triumph for this theory that it predicts chlorine molecules to be diatomic, in agreement with observation. The monatomic molecule, Cl, is unstable because its electron configuration is not like that of an inert gas. Molecules containing more than two chlorine atoms, such as Cl_3 or Cl_4, are likewise unstable. After the diatomic Cl_2 molecule has been formed, there are no more half-filled orbitals that can be used for further bond formation, and the approach of an additional chlorine atom or of another Cl_2 molecule does not result in stable molecule formation.

Bonds resulting from the sharing of pairs of electrons by two atoms are referred to as *covalent** bonds. There are many other examples. Hydrogen molecules (H_2) are known to consist of two hydrogen atoms. This fact can be explained by assuming that the two atoms share their electrons, so that each hydrogen atom acquires a share in a stable, helium-like electron configuration.

$$H\cdot \,\,+\,\, \cdot H \,\,\longrightarrow\,\, H\,\,\boxed{..}\,\,H$$

Compare this with

$$He:$$

Molecules of the halogens other than chlorine, such as fluorine or iodine, are also diatomic. This fact can be explained by assuming the formation of a covalent bond, analogous to the bond between two chlorine atoms:

$$:\overset{..}{\underset{..}{F}}\,\,\boxed{..}\,\,\overset{..}{\underset{..}{F}}: \qquad\qquad :\overset{..}{\underset{..}{I}}\,\,\boxed{..}\,\,\overset{..}{\underset{..}{I}}:$$

It is not necessary that the atoms sharing the electron pair be identical. For example, a number of diatomic *interhalogen* compounds are known; here again, the two halogen atoms are thought to be joined by a covalent bond, as illustrated for *iodine bromide:*

$$:\overset{..}{\underset{..}{I}}\cdot \,\,+\,\, \cdot\overset{..}{\underset{..}{Br}}: \,\,\longrightarrow\,\, :\overset{..}{\underset{..}{I}}\,\,\boxed{..}\,\,\overset{..}{\underset{..}{Br}}:$$

iodine atom   bromine atom   iodine bromide

* From the Latin roots *co-* and *valens,* meaning something like "strong through sharing."

Another example is the diatomic substance *hydrogen chloride* (HCl). One may theorize that the molecules of this substance are diatomic because, by the sharing of an electron pair, the hydrogen atom achieves a stable helium-like configuration, and the chlorine atom a stable octet.

$$ H\ \square\ +\ \square\ \overline{Cl}\ \longrightarrow\ H\ \cdots\ \overline{Cl} $$

Covalent Molecules Consisting of More than Two Atoms

In theory, an atom can form as many covalent bonds as it has half-filled outer orbitals. For example, we saw that hydrogen and chlorine atoms each have *one* half-filled outer orbital, hence will form only *one* covalent bond.

$$ H\square \qquad \vdots\overline{Cl}\square $$

Oxygen atoms, on the other hand, have *two* half-filled orbitals, hence can form *two* covalent bonds.

$$ \square\overline{O}\square $$

An oxygen atom can, therefore, combine with two hydrogen atoms to form a molecule with the formula H_2O, in which both hydrogen atoms are joined to a central oxygen atom.

$$ H\square\ +\ \square\overline{O}\square\ +\ \square H\ \longrightarrow\ H\cdots\overline{O}\cdots H $$

water

Physical measurements have shown that this is indeed the correct picture for the water molecule.

Similarly, nitrogen atoms, with three half-filled orbitals, can form three bonds.

$$ \square\overline{N}\square $$

If the nitrogen atom combines with three hydrogen atoms, a molecule with the formula NH_3 is formed, in which all three of the hydrogen atoms are bonded to the nitrogen atom.

$$ H\square\ +\ \square\overline{N}\square\ +\ \square H\ \longrightarrow\ H\cdots\overline{N}\cdots H $$
$$ +\qquad\qquad\qquad\qquad\ \vdots $$
$$ \square\qquad\qquad\qquad\qquad\ H $$
$$ H $$

ammonia, NH_3

And in fact, this is the correct formula for the familiar substance, ammonia.

Perhaps most interesting of all is the carbon atom, which we represent as having four half-filled orbitals.

$$\cdot \overset{\cdot}{\underset{\cdot}{C}} \cdot$$

When such an atom combines with, say, four hydrogen atoms, all four of the outer orbitals are involved in bond formation.

$$\begin{array}{c} H \\ \vdots \\ H \cdots C \cdots H \\ \vdots \\ H \end{array}$$

methane, CH_4

The formula, CH_4, correctly represents the molecules of the known substance methane, which is a principal component of natural gas.

It is possible to write down a literally endless number of molecular formulas in which the atoms are joined by covalent bonds. Some additional formulas, showing molecules of somewhat greater complexity, are listed in the following table. The table also gives the names and boiling points of actual compounds having these formulas.

Formula	Actual compound
$\begin{array}{c} H \\ \vdots \\ H \cdots C \cdots \overset{\cdots}{\underset{\cdots}{Cl}} \\ \vdots \\ H \end{array}$	CH_3Cl, methyl chloride b.p. $-24.2°C$
$\begin{array}{c} \overset{\cdots}{\underset{\cdots}{Cl}} \\ \vdots \\ \overset{\cdots}{\underset{\cdots}{Cl}} \cdots C \cdots \overset{\cdots}{\underset{\cdots}{Cl}} \\ \vdots \\ \overset{\cdots}{\underset{\cdots}{Cl}} \end{array}$	CCl_4, carbon tetrachloride b.p. $76°C$
$\begin{array}{cc} H & H \\ \vdots & \vdots \\ H \cdots C \cdots & C \cdots H \\ \vdots & \vdots \\ H & H \end{array}$	C_2H_6, ethane b.p. $-88.3°C$
$\begin{array}{cc} \overset{\cdots}{} & \overset{\cdots}{} \\ H \cdots N \cdots & N \cdots H \\ \vdots & \vdots \\ H & H \end{array}$	N_2H_4, hydrazine b.p. $113.5°C$
$\begin{array}{ccccc} H & H & H & H & H \\ \vdots & \vdots & \vdots & \vdots & \vdots \\ H \cdots C \cdots & C \cdots & C \cdots & C \cdots & C \cdots H \\ \vdots & \vdots & \vdots & \vdots & \vdots \\ H & H & H & H & H \end{array}$	C_5H_{12}, *normal* pentane b.p. $36.2°C$

The theory that atoms can acquire stable electron configurations through sharing of electrons with other atoms is well established. In the great majority of cases, if one writes a "paper formula" that looks stable (each atom has an inert gas electron configuration), a corresponding actual substance almost invariably exists in nature or can be prepared in the laboratory. On the other hand, if the "paper formula" is such that some of the atoms do not have an inert gas configuration, a corresponding actual substance is either not known, or else is highly reactive.

For example, it is known that a substance with the formula CH_3 is not capable of stable existence. CH_3 molecules exist for only a small fraction of a second before they react to form more stable molecules. An explanation for the lack of stability is suggested by the "paper formula":

$$H\ \colon\!\colon C\ \text{with H above and below}$$

The carbon atom still has a half-filled orbital which can be used to form a covalent bond to some other atom or group of atoms. Thus, two CH_3 units will couple according to the equation:

ethane

Double Bonds and Triple Bonds

It is possible in principle that two atoms be held together by more than a single covalent bond. Nitrogen molecules (N_2) are a case in point. The nitrogen atoms achieve a stable octet of electrons by the sharing of three electron pairs, to form a *triple* bond.

2 nitrogen atoms

nitrogen molecule; the atoms are joined by a triple bond

Similarly, in carbon dioxide (CO_2) each atom achieves a stable octet if the carbon atom is joined to the two oxygen atoms by double bonds:

double bonds

The formation of double or triple bonds between two atoms is not at all uncommon. A double bond is nearly twice as strong as a single bond, and a triple bond is nearly three times as strong. The increase in bond strength is always accompanied by a decrease in the distance between the bonded atoms.

A much-studied example is a series of compounds with the formulas C_2H_6, C_2H_4, and C_2H_2. The "paper formulas," chemical names, and other properties of these compounds are listed in the table.

Formula and name	Boiling point	Energy of the bond between the carbon atoms (calories)	Carbon-carbon bond distance (cm)
H H H C C H H H C_2H_6, ethane	−88.3°C	80,000	1.54′× 10^{-8}
H H C C H H C_2H_4, ethylene	−103.9°C	145,000	1.33 × 10^{-8}
H C C H C_2H_2, acetylene	−88.5°C	198,000	1.20 × 10^{-8}

Note that the bonding of the carbon atoms changes from a single bond in C_2H_6 to a triple bond in C_2H_2, and that the molecules depicted by these formulas are capable of stable existence. Each carbon atom is surrounded by an octet of electrons. The strength of the bond joining the two carbon atoms is measured by the *bond energy*, which is the amount of energy required to break the bond. The data in the table show the progressive increase in bond energy from single bond to double bond to triple bond. They also show the decrease in the distance between the centers of the carbon atoms.

Chemical and Physical Properties of Covalent Compounds

The properties of covalent compounds contrast sharply with those of ionic compounds, reflecting directly the difference in the nature of the bonds holding the atoms together. It was pointed out earlier, for example, that the ionic compound sodium chloride melts at 800°C. Solid methane, on the other hand, melts at −183°C (983° lower). This large difference in melting point stems from a fundamental difference in the melting process for the two classes of compounds. In ionic compounds melting actually involves the rupture of bonds between ions, since the orderly network of bonds between positive and negative ions which exists in the crystalline solid is disrupted on melting. It takes quite a bit of energy to rupture the ionic bonds, and it is no wonder then that high temperatures are required.

In contrast, the melting and boiling of covalent compounds does *not* involve the rupture of interatomic bonds; it involves merely the separation of the covalent molecules, the molecules themselves remaining intact. The intermolecular attractions which produce solid or liquid aggregates of covalent molecules are generally much weaker than the attractions involved in ionic or covalent bonds; and as a consequence, covalently bonded substances have relatively low melting and boiling points.

In the gas phase, covalent compounds, in contrast to ionic ones, consist of definite molecules with a definite molecular formula. Thus, methane gas consists entirely of CH_4 units, in contrast to gaseous sodium chloride which consists of $NaCl$, Na_2Cl_2, Na_3Cl_3, etc. The electron requirements of each atom in the methane molecule are fully satisfied, so there is no tendency to form additional bonds to other atoms.

The response of covalently bonded substances to electrical currents is also quite different from that of ionic substances under similar conditions. Melts or solutions of ionic substances, it will be recalled, permit the passage of electric currents. On the other hand, covalent substances in the liquid state do not appreciably conduct electricity. This behavior is clearly in agreement with our model, according to which charged ions are completely absent in covalent substances. Similarly, solutions of covalent substances in water are poor conductors, unless the covalent substance reacts with the water to produce ions.

The speed at which a substance is transformed into new substances by a chemical reaction can give additional information about the nature of the bonds involved. If reaction is slow, requiring minutes or even hours for completion, then it is safe to conclude that the process of converting the reagent molecules to the product molecules requires the breaking of a covalent bond. On the other hand, if the reaction involves the combination of ions, it is likely to be extremely rapid.

Brief Discussion of Ionic and Covalent Compounds in Terms of the Periodic Chart

We have seen that it is possible to determine whether a given compound is ionic or covalent, because of the sharp contrast in the properties of the two types of compounds. The question now arises whether it is possible to *predict* the nature of the bonding in a given compound.

In seeking an answer to this question, we recall that the covalent bond was first conceived of to explain the bonding of *identical* atoms (as in H_2 or Cl_2), and that the ionic bond was postulated for compounds of such dissimilar elements as the alkali metals and the halogens. In terms of the periodic chart (page 122), ionic compounds are likely to be formed between the metallic elements on the left of the chart and the nonmetallic ones on the right—excepting, of course, the inert gases. Considering only the main-group elements, covalent bonds are formed:

1. ... between identical atoms,
2. ... between atoms belonging to the same column of the periodic chart, such as iodine and bromine,
3. ... between atoms belonging to adjacent columns, such as aluminum and carbon,
4. ... between any two nonmetallic atoms, such as carbon and oxygen, hydrogen and nitrogen, or boron and chlorine.

Other Types of Bonds

The coordinate-covalent bond

The coordinate-covalent bond is an interesting variation on the covalent bond in which one atom supplies *both* of the bonding electrons. A case in point is the compound formed between ammonia (NH_3) and boron trifluoride (BF_3). The structure of the ammonia molecule has already been discussed; it is as follows:

$$H \cdot\cdot N \cdot\cdot H \quad \longleftarrow \text{unshared electron pair}$$

Note that three electron pairs are used to form the N-H bonds, but that the fourth electron pair is not being shared by any other atom.

Next let us consider the bonding in boron trifluoride:

$$:F\cdot + \cdot B\cdot + \cdot F: \qquad \qquad \longleftarrow \text{vacant orbital}$$

$$+$$

$$:F: \qquad \longrightarrow \quad :F \cdot\cdot B \cdot\cdot F:$$

$$:F:$$

Originally, the boron atom has three outer electrons. Through sharing of electrons with the fluorine atoms it can acquire a share in six electrons, but still needs two electrons to complete the octet. These two electrons can be furnished by the ammonia molecule:

$$H \quad :F: \qquad \qquad H \quad :F:$$

$$H \cdot\cdot N: \;\; + \;\; B \cdot\cdot F: \;\; \longrightarrow \;\; H \cdot\cdot N \cdot\cdot B \cdot\cdot F:$$

$$H \quad :F: \qquad \qquad H \quad :F:$$

These orbitals overlap   and   a coordinate-covalent bond results.

The coordinate-covalent bond formed by the blending of the two atomic orbitals is just like an ordinary covalent bond, except that the nitrogen atom has supplied *both* electrons.

In this connection it is interesting to note that boron trifluoride is a moderately stable compound, even though the boron atom does not have an octet of electrons. Substances the formation of which violates the octet rule are occasionally found. But such substances generally react further to form substances in which the octet rule is satisfied.

Compounds with both ionic and covalent bonds

So far in our discussion of bonding we have confined ourselves to molecules in which there are *only* ionic bonds or *only* covalent bonds. There are, of course, numerous substances in which bonds of both types exist simultaneously.

Potassium hydroxide is an example. The molecule, KOH, contains one ionic bond and one covalent bond. First the hydrogen atom is bonded to the oxygen atom by a covalent bond to form the unit:

$$\overset{\cdot\cdot}{\underset{\cdot\cdot}{\cdot\,O}}\, \cdot\cdot\, H$$

Then the potassium atom transfers an electron to form the stable molecule:

$$K^{\oplus} \quad \overset{\cdot\cdot}{\underset{\cdot\cdot}{:O}}\, \cdot\cdot\, H^{\ominus}$$

Thus, when potassium hydroxide is dissolved in water it dissociates into potassium ions (K⁺) and hydroxide ions:

$$\overset{\cdot\cdot}{\underset{\cdot\cdot}{:O}}\, \cdot\cdot\, H^{\ominus}$$

A second example is furnished by silver nitrate, which has the formula $AgNO_3$. The three oxygen atoms are bonded to the nitrogen to form the unit NO_3, to which a silver atom transfers an electron to form NO_3^-.

$$Ag^{\oplus} \left[\begin{array}{c} \overset{\diamond\diamond}{O}\quad\overset{\diamond\diamond}{O} \\ \diagdown\;\diagup \\ N \\ | \\ :O: \end{array} \right]^{\ominus}$$

Solutions of silver nitrate are thus composed of silver ions (Ag⁺) and nitrate ions (NO_3^-). Many other common substances exhibit this kind of dual bonding, some of which have been previously mentioned. For example, calcium sulfate ($Ca^{++}SO_4^=$), potassium carbonate [$(K^+)_2CO_3^=$], and sodium azide ($Na^+N_3^-$).

14 *The Architecture of*
Covalent Molecules

ONE OF the most exciting applications of our knowledge concerning the
nature of the chemical bond is that it enables us to describe the structure
of molecules in considerable detail. By structure we mean the organization
of the atoms within a given molecule. Previously we had concerned ourselves chiefly with the *composition* of molecules. But knowing the composition of a molecule is not the same as knowing its structure, any more
than knowing the quantities of materials involved in a building is the same
as knowing its architecture.

A most satisfying chapter in the history of chemistry has been the
growth in our knowledge of the structure of even the most complex molecules. Substances whose names are ordinary household words, such as

penicillin, chlorophyll, or D.D.T., consist of molecules composed of dozens of atoms, and our knowledge of the architecture of these molecules is quite exact. Even such extremely complex substances as the proteins are beginning to yield the secrets of their construction.

The diagrams of molecular structure which will be presented in this and the following chapter are remarkably detailed when one considers that all the information upon which they are based is of an extremely indirect kind.

The Inadequacy of the Molecular Formula

In the preceding chapters we considered the forces binding atoms together to form molecules. We learned that there are two main types of chemical bonding, the ionic bond and the covalent bond, and that these two types of bonding lead to quite different results. Ionic bonding results in the formation of large crystalline aggregates of indefinite size. On the other hand, covalent bonding leads to the formation of definite molecular units in which specific numbers of atoms are joined together to form discrete molecules. These molecular units can be represented by molecular formulas, such as CH_4, H_2O, or Cl_2, in which the elements are written in a completely arbitrary order, regardless of how they are actually joined in the molecule. The information conveyed by this type of representation is merely the number of atoms which have combined to form one molecule of the substance. The molecular formula tells us nothing about the way in which the atoms are linked.

But the details of the construction of the molecule are important—a fact which was appreciated early in the development of chemistry. The molecular formula, which tells us nothing about the molecular architecture, is therefore inadequate. One of the simplest ways of appreciating this fact is to consider that two entirely different substances can have exactly the same number and kind of atoms in their molecules. For example, the two substances, dimethyl ether and ethyl alcohol, both have the molecular formula C_2H_6O. Ethyl alcohol is the active ingredient in alcoholic beverages; dimethyl ether is chemically similar to the ether used in surgical anesthesia. Ethyl alcohol is a liquid boiling at 78°C and is infinitely soluble in water; dimethyl ether is a gas at room temperature and is only slightly soluble in water. Ethyl alcohol reacts with metallic sodium; dimethyl ether does not. Clearly, these two materials are different substances, even though their molecular formulas are identical.

Structural Isomerism

Substances with the same molecular formula but different physical and chemical properties are called *isomers.** We shall state the hypothesis that isomerism can arise when it is possible to build up molecules of different architecture from the same set of atoms without violating the octet rule.

It will be recalled that covalently bonded molecules are capable of stable existence if each atom has acquired an inert-gas electron configuration. In terms of our hypothesis, this means that every possible arrangement of the atoms in which the octet rule is satisfied represents potentially a stable isomer. If it is possible to arrange the atoms in only one way while satisfying this requirement, then only one substance with this molecular formula is expected to exist. But if there are several alternative arrangements, the existence of several substances with this molecular formula is anticipated.

Let us now consider in detail the two isomeric substances with the molecular formula C_2H_6O, namely, ethyl alcohol and dimethyl ether. Molecules with the formula C_2H_6O consist of nine atoms of three different elements. The possible number of different arrangements of these atoms is very large if no attention is paid to the octet rule. But only two arrangements conform to the rule. They are as follows:

$$
\begin{array}{cc}
\begin{array}{cc} H & H \\ | & | \\ H-C-C-\overline{O}-H \\ | & | \\ H & H \end{array}
&
\begin{array}{cc} H & H \\ | & | \\ H-C-\overline{O}-C-H \\ | & | \\ H & H \end{array}
\\[1em]
I & II
\end{array}
$$

In writing structural formulas I and II, we have adopted a convenient shorthand. Filled two-electron orbitals, which up to now have been represented by a box containing two dots, are simply indicated by a dash.

It is gratifying to know that the number of actual substances with the formula C_2H_6O is exactly equal to the number of stable structural formulas that one can write for molecules with this composition. There are two substances and two formulas. Assuming that these formulas actually represent the molecular architecture of ethyl alcohol and dimethyl ether, the prob-

---

* Derived from the Greek roots *iso* ("equal") and *meros* ("part"); i.e., the molecules of the two substances are constructed from the same (atomic) building materials, and in the same proportions.

lem to be solved is that of assigning the appropriate structural formula to the right substance.

Assignment of structural formula

This problem can be solved because *molecular structure has chemical consequences.* A chemical reaction involves the making and breaking of bonds between atoms. Since the structural formula depicts the bonds in the molecule, it provides information about the reactions which a substance with such a structure would be expected to undergo.

How do the bonds in structure I differ from those in structure II? Structure I contains an O—H bond, while structure II does not. In structure I the two carbon atoms are linked directly, while in structure II they are separated by an oxygen atom. Both structures contain several C—H bonds and at least one C—O bond.

When we know the chemical reactions of each of the two substances, we will be able to assign the appropriate structural formula to each substance by taking advantage of these differences. For example, one and only one of the two substances is expected to exhibit the reactions characteristic of an O—H bond. Let us find out whether this is in fact the case. The first question which we must answer is: What *are* the chemical properties of an O—H bond? Common sense would dictate that this question can be answered by studying the chemical properties of a molecule in which all the bonds are O—H bonds. The water molecule is such a molecule. One of the characteristic properties of water molecules is that they react readily with alkali metal atoms; hydrogen gas is evolved, and an alkali hydroxide, such as NaOH, is formed.

$$H—\overline{O}—H \qquad \begin{array}{c} H \\ | \\ H—C—H \\ | \\ H \end{array}$$

water

methane

The ready reaction with alkali metals is characteristic of the O—H bond but not of the C—H bond. Methane (CH_4), which has only C—H bonds, does not react readily with sodium.

As mentioned before, one of the two isomeric substances, ethyl alcohol, reacts with sodium in the manner characteristic of an O—H bond, while the other, dimethyl ether, does not. Therefore the substance, ethyl alcohol, must be assigned structure I, since this has an O—H bond, leaving structure II to be assigned to the isomeric substance, dimethyl ether.

The accuracy of these assignments may be tested further by carrying out a chemical reaction, the products of which can be predicted correctly only if the structures are assigned correctly. A suitable reaction is that of ethers and alcohols with hydrogen iodide. For structures I and II, the predicted reactions are as follows:

Structure I:

$$
\begin{array}{ccc}
\underset{\substack{|\\ \text{H}}}{\overset{\substack{\text{H}\\ |}}{\text{H—C}}}\text{—}\underset{\substack{|\\ \text{H}}}{\overset{\substack{\text{H}\\ |}}{\text{C}}}\text{—}\overline{\text{O}}\text{—H} & + & \text{H—}\overline{\text{I}}| \\
\end{array}
\longrightarrow
\;
\underset{\substack{|\\ \text{H}}}{\overset{\substack{\text{H}\\ |}}{\text{H—C}}}\text{—}\underset{\substack{|\\ \text{H}}}{\overset{\substack{\text{H}\\ |}}{\text{C}}}\text{—}\overline{\text{I}}|
\;+\;
\text{H—}\overline{\text{O}}\text{—H}
$$

Hydrogen iodide

Ethyl iodide

Structure II:

$$
\underset{\substack{|\\ \text{H}}}{\overset{\substack{\text{H}\\ |}}{\text{H—C}}}\text{—}\overline{\text{O}}\text{—}\underset{\substack{|\\ \text{H}}}{\overset{\substack{\text{H}\\ |}}{\text{C}}}\text{—H}
\;+\;
2\,\text{H—}\overline{\text{I}}|
\longrightarrow
2\,\text{H—}\underset{\substack{|\\ \text{H}}}{\overset{\substack{\text{H}\\ |}}{\text{C}}}\text{—}\overline{\text{I}}|
\;+\;
\text{H—}\overline{\text{O}}\text{—H}
$$

Hydrogen iodide

Methyl iodide

The equations show that if we had a substance with structure I, reaction with hydrogen iodide (HI) would produce a substance, ethyl iodide, with the formula C_2H_5I; if we had a substance with structure II, treatment with HI would result in the production of two molecules of methyl iodide, CH_3I, for every molecule of starting material. When the actual substances are treated with hydrogen iodide, ethyl alcohol reacts to give ethyl iodide, and methyl ether gives methyl iodide. The formation of ethyl iodide from ethyl alcohol, and of methyl iodide from dimethyl ether, can be explained only if the true molecular structure of ethyl alcohol is that depicted in structure I, and if the molecular structure of dimethyl ether is that depicted in II. Our assignment of structure is therefore complete.

Isomeric substances such as ethyl alcohol and dimethyl ether, *the molecules of which differ in the order in which the atoms are connected,* are called *structural isomers.* Thousands of examples of structural isomerism are known. A few of these will serve to illustrate the principles involved.

Let us first consider a series of organic compounds known as the *aliphatic hydrocarbons.* The simplest of these compounds is methane, the structure of which is shown on page 167. Only one structure can be written which satisfies the octet rule, and indeed, only one compound with the formula CH_4 exists.

The next member of this series is ethane, C_2H_6, for which again only one structure, III, can be written, as the reader should verify for himself. The next member is propane, C_3H_8, for which the only possible structure is IV.

$$\begin{array}{ccc} & H & H \\ & | & | \\ H- & C-C & -H \\ & | & | \\ & H & H \end{array} \qquad \begin{array}{cccc} & H & H & H \\ & | & | & | \\ H- & C-C-C & -H \\ & | & | & | \\ & H & H & H \end{array}$$

III. Ethane   IV. Propane

However, when a fourth carbon atom is added to the molecule to give C_4H_{10} there are two ways of organizing these atoms. These are illustrated in V and VI. And indeed, two substances with the formula C_4H_{10} are known: *normal* butane, b.p. $-0.5°C$; and *iso*-butane, b.p. $-12°C$.

$$\begin{array}{ccccc} & H & H & H & H \\ & | & | & | & | \\ H- & C-C-C-C & -H \\ & | & | & | & | \\ & H & H & H & H \end{array} \qquad \begin{array}{ccccc} & H & & H & & H \\ & | & & | & & | \\ H- & C & - & C & - & C & -H \\ & | & & | & & | \\ & H & & | & & H \\ & & & H-C-H \\ & & & | \\ & & & H \end{array}$$

V. *Normal butane*   VI. *Iso-butane*

As the number of atoms in the molecular formula increases, the number of possible arrangements becomes very large indeed. Thus, while there are only two structural isomers for the hydrocarbon C_4H_{10}, both of which are known, one can write thirty-five different structural isomers for the hydrocarbon C_9H_{20}, and 62,491,178,805,831 isomers for $C_{40}H_{82}$. In agreement with the theory, thirty-five different substances with the formula C_9H_{20} have actually been prepared and identified. One must confess, however, that the theoretical number of isomers has not yet been prepared and identified for $C_{40}H_{82}$.

It must be emphasized that throughout this section we have been concerned solely with the order in which the atoms are linked. A structural formula such as V is intended to show only the organization of the atoms within the molecule—i.e., which atom is bonded to which; it is *not* intended to pictorialize the three-dimensional molecule. In this representation the angles between the bonds may be drawn in any arbitrary manner. For example, we must not imply from V that the carbon atoms in *normal* butane are arranged in a straight line, but merely that they are connected in the order indicated. Structures such as VII, in which the angles between the carbon atoms have been drawn differently, do not represent additional structural isomers because the order in which the atoms are linked is still the same.

$$\begin{array}{ccccc} & H & H & H & H \\ & | & | & | & | \\ H- & C- & C- & C- & C-H \\ & | & | & | & | \\ & H & H & H & H \end{array}$$

V

$$\begin{array}{cc} H & H \\ | & | \\ H-C- & C-H \\ | & \\ H & H \\ & | \\ H-C- & C-H \\ | & | \\ H & H \end{array}$$

VII

Structural formulas V and VII represent the same molecule.

The Tetrahedral Carbon Atom

In the preceding sections we studied the organization of the atoms within the molecule. We found it possible to discuss this problem fruitfully without recourse to the relationship that the atoms might bear to one another in three-dimensional space. That this relationship might be important in certain cases was recognized almost simultaneously by Louis Pasteur in France and Friedrich Augustus Kekulé von Stradonitz in Germany. Kekulé, writing in 1859, pointed out that the incompleteness of the structural formula may be avoided if instead of arranging the four bonds of the carbon atom in a plane, we place them so that they run out and end in the corners of a tetrahedron. In 1860, Louis Pasteur, at that time interested in a phenomenon known as optical activity, suggested an explanation which involved the three-dimensional arrangement of the atoms in those molecules that exhibit optical activity.

These early speculations were developed into a coherent theory of molecular structure by two chemists working quite independently, one in Holland and the other in France. In 1874, J. H. van't Hoff and J. A. LeBel both published articles to explain the phenomenon of optical activity. This phenomenon will be considered later. What concerns us at this time is that their conclusions reached far beyond the field of optical activity and applied to a wide variety of molecules.

In accord with Kekulé's earlier suggestion, van't Hoff and LeBel postulated that the four covalent bonds which the carbon atom is capable of forming are directed toward the corners of a regular tetrahedron, a regular geometrical solid shown in Figure 14-1. The carbon atom is located at the

Fig. 14-1. A regular tetrahedron.

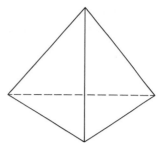

center of the tetrahedron, and the four atoms to which it is bonded are located at the corners. This arrangement is illustrated in Figure 14-2, using the methane molecule as an example.

When a model of the tetrahedral methane molecule is constructed, the angle between the carbon atom and any two hydrogen atoms

$$\text{C}$$
$$\overset{\curvearrowright}{\text{H} \qquad \text{H}}$$

is found to be 109° 28′. This angle is called the "tetrahedral bond angle." There is very good experimental evidence that in the actual methane molecule the bond angles are very close to the expected value of 109° 28′. Moreover, bond angles have been measured for a large number of other carbon compounds of the same type, and in every case the angles have turned out to be very nearly tetrahedral.

The distances between the centers of the carbon atom and the hydrogen atoms, the so-called "C—H bond distances," have also been measured for the methane molecule. There are four carbon-hydrogen bonds in the methane molecule, and the four C—H bond distances have been found to be identical: 1.09×10^{-8} cm. This equality is consistent with a regular tetrahedral structure.

Fig. 14-2. Tetrahedral structure of the methane molecule.

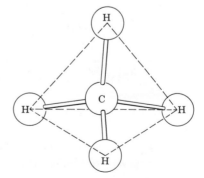

Another piece of evidence which indicates a symmetrical structure (such as a tetrahedral one) is that the chemical reactivity of all four C—H bonds is identical.

If instead of a hydrogen atom, a second carbon atom is bonded to the first, as for example in ethane (C_2H_6), the C—C bond distance is found to be 1.54×10^{-8} cm, the C—H distances are again 1.09×10^{-8} cm, and the bond angles are again tetrahedral. The ethane molecule can therefore be represented by Figure 14-3.

If now one joins three carbon atoms to form the propane molecule (C_3H_8), one obtains a molecule which can be depicted as in Figure 14-4. The two isomers of the next higher hydrocarbon, butane (C_4H_{10}), are depicted in Figure 14-5.

It is worthwhile to contrast the three-dimensional picture of the normal butane molecule, Figure 14-5, with its representation by means of structural formulas as shown on page 170. In the structural formula, the bond angles and distances are necessarily arbitrary, and the only information conveyed is the order in which the atoms are connected. The three-dimensional formula conveys not only this information, but also the bond angles and bond distances. Thus, we see in Figure 14-5 that the carbon skeleton in *normal* butane is not straight nor bent at an angle of 90° as might be inferred from V and VII, but forms a zig-zag with tetrahedral angles as required by the tetrahedral nature of carbon bonds.

The concept of three-dimensional molecules is one of the most impor-

Fig. 14-3. Ball-and-stick model of the ethane molecule. The dark balls represent carbon atoms and the light balls hydrogen atoms.

Fig. 14-4. Ball-and-stick model of the propane molecule.

tant achievements of chemistry and ranks near the very top on any list of noteworthy advances in science. Considering the elusiveness of the individual molecules, the detail with which their architecture can be depicted is remarkable indeed.

The concept of fixed bond directions is, of course, not restricted to molecules containing carbon atoms, but applies to all covalent molecules. Thus, in the water molecule the three atoms are not arranged in a straight

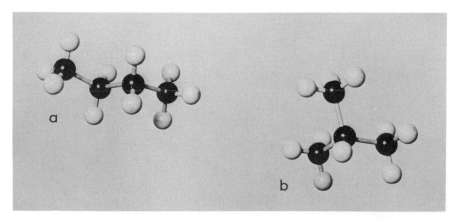

Fig. 14-5. Ball-and-stick models of the two isomers of C_4H_{10}. (a) *Normal* butane; (b) *iso-*butane.

Fig. 14-6. Ball-and-stick model of the water molecule. The dark
ball represents an oxygen atom.

line as might be inferred from the structural formula, but the three atoms
form an angle which is just a little smaller than the tetrahedral angle.

There is some evidence that the two unshared pairs of electrons of the
oxygen atom (page 156) move in orbitals which are directed toward the
remaining two corners of the tetrahedron. Likewise in ammonia (NH_3,

Fig. 14-7. Ball-and-stick model
of the ammonia molecule. The
stick pointing up indicates the direction of the unshared pair of
electrons.

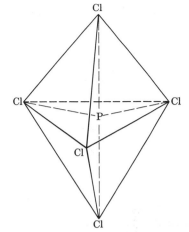

Fig. 14-8. Diagram of the phosphorus pentachloride molecule.

page 156), the bond angles are again very nearly tetrahedral, with hydrogen atoms occupying three of the four corners, and the single unshared pair of electrons the fourth. However, it must not be assumed that all bond angles are close to the tetrahedral value of 109° 28'. For example, gaseous phosphorus pentachloride (PCl_5) has the structure shown in Figure 14-8.

Directed Bonds and Atomic Orbitals

The picture of three-dimensional molecules with bonds oriented in specific directions was developed long before the theory of atomic orbitals discussed in Chapter 11, but is wholly consistent with it.

It will be recalled that certain atomic orbitals, for example the p and d orbitals, have definite directional characteristics. When these orbitals are involved in the formation of covalent bonds, one would expect their directional characteristics to be reflected in the relative positions of the atoms involved in the bond. Thus, if the atomic orbitals that form the bonds are two p orbitals which are separated by an angle of 90°, one would expect that the bonds formed by these orbitals also form an angle of 90°. Molecules are known for which this expectation is borne out to a good approximation. For example, the H—S—H bond angle in H_2S is 92° 16', indicating that the p orbitals of the sulfur atom are involved in forming the bonds. Bonding of this type is illustrated in Figure 14-9. In many other cases, however, the bond angles are quite different from those predicted on the basis of the orbitals in the free atom. Here one must assume that the atomic orbitals are considerably modified by the bond formation.

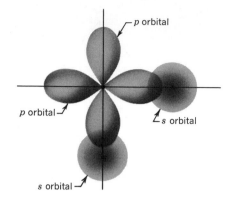

p orbital

p orbital

s orbital

s orbital

Fig. 14-9. Molecule of the type H_2X, formed by overlapping of two p-orbitals of X with the s-orbital of hydrogen. The p-orbitals shown are 2p-orbitals. ● = atomic nucleus.

Geometrical Isomerism

A second type of isomerism that was quite puzzling for a long time is exemplified by the existence of the two substances, maleic acid and fumaric acid. Both acids have the molecular formula $C_4H_4O_4$, and the arrangement of the atoms is the same in both compounds; that is, the two compounds are *not* structural isomers. Yet they are clearly different compounds: maleic acid melts at 135°C, and fumaric acid at 287°C. Maleic acid is readily converted by heating to a new substance, called maleic anhydride ($C_4H_2O_3$), which is formed by the loss of water; fumaric acid is converted to the anhydride only with difficulty. Since the two substances are clearly different yet are not structural isomers, wherein lies the difference? Van't Hoff suggested that the difference was due to the spatial arrangement of the atoms in the two molecules.

In order to understand van't Hoff's theory of geometrical isomerism, it is necessary first to consider the rotation of two groups of atoms about the covalent bond joining them. It has been found that two groups of atoms, when joined by a *single* bond, are free to rotate with respect to one another. Thus, in ethane,

$$H-\underset{\underset{\displaystyle H}{|}}{\overset{\overset{\displaystyle H}{|}}{C}}----\underset{\underset{\displaystyle H}{|}}{\overset{\overset{\displaystyle H}{|}}{C}}-H$$

each group can rotate about the axis of the C—C covalent bond, just as two wheels may rotate independently on a common axle. (See Figure 14-10.) If, however, the two carbon atoms are joined by two covalent bonds (a double bond), as is the case in ethylene (C_2H_4), this rotation is no longer possible, and the structure is a relatively rigid one. To pursue the

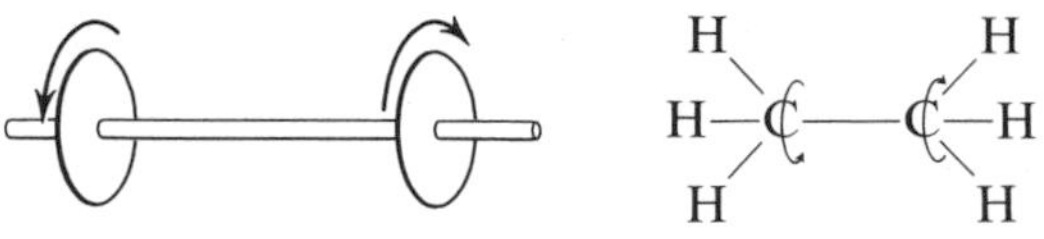

Fig. 14-10. Free rotation about the C—C bond axis in ethane.

analogy of the two wheels, if the wheels were joined by two separate axles, as shown in Figure 14-11, they would no longer be free to rotate with respect to one another.

Fig. 14-11. Restricted rotation about the C=C axis in ethylene.

Since maleic and fumaric acid both contain a double bond, it was van't Hoff's hypothesis that the two molecules differed in the way in which the other atoms in the molecule were arranged about this rigid spine. He proposed the following structures for the two acids:

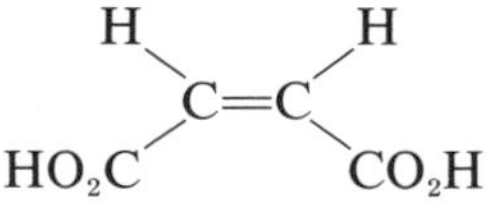

VIII. Maleic acid

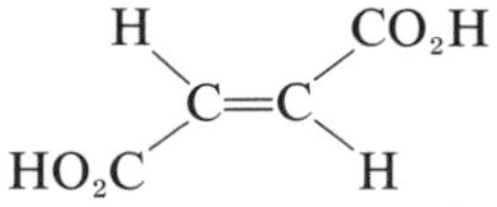

IX. Fumaric acid

The two groups joined by the double bond are not free to rotate with respect to one another, so that the groups retain their relative positions in space, and the two molecules are distinct. In the case of maleic acid, the two hydrogen atoms are on the same side of the double bond (*cis*), while in fumaric acid they are on opposite sides (*trans*). Many other examples of this type of geometrical isomerism about a double bond are known.

The freedom of rotation about single bonds of course makes it impossible for isomerism of this type to arise in analogous compounds containing a single bond instead of the double bond. For example, it is possible to write two paper formulas for succinic acid, $C_4H_6O_4$, which are analogous to those shown above for maleic acid and fumaric acid:

X.
(CO₂H groups on same side)

XI.
(CO₂H groups on opposite side)

In fact, only one substance with the structural formula of succinic acid is known. This is readily understood because rotation about the single bond rapidly interconverts structures X and XI. Thus, an actual sample of succinic acid consists of molecules with all possible relative orientations of the CO_2H groups.

The Asymmetric Carbon Atom

There is yet another type of isomerism which arises out of the geometrical character of the tetrahedral carbon atom. When the four atoms or groups attached to the carbon atom are all different, the molecule becomes asymmetric. By this is meant that the molecule and its mirror image are no longer identical, and therefore two nonsuperimposable forms can exist. Consider, for example, the substance, alanine, which contains a carbon

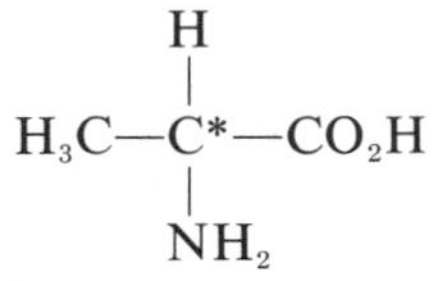

$$H_3C—\overset{\overset{\displaystyle H}{|}}{\underset{\underset{\displaystyle NH_2}{|}}{C^*}}—CO_2H$$

XII. Alanine

atom (C*) having four different groups attached to it: CH_3, NH_2, H, and CO_2H. Two different structures exist for this molecule, one of which is the mirror image of the other. These structures are shown in Figure 14-12. The two isomers of alanine differ from one another in the same way as does the right hand from the left hand. How does this difference manifest itself? On gross examination, the two isomers appear to be identical. For example, they have the same density and the same solubility in water, and they react at equal rates with symmetrical molecules. However, a difference does manifest itself when the two isomers react with asymmetric molecules, or when they interact with polarized light.

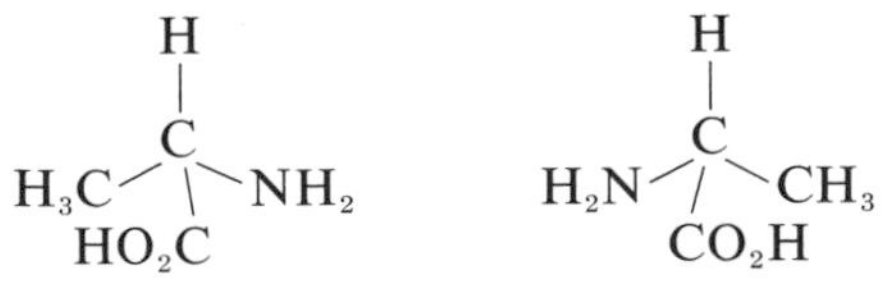

Fig. 14-12. The two forms of alanine.

A beam of light is said to be polarized if the wave motion associated with the light beam is restricted to a single plane. When such a beam passes through a solution containing one form of an asymmetric molecule, the plane of polarization is rotated in a clockwise direction. When the beam passes through a solution containing the mirror image form, the plane of polarization is rotated in a counterclockwise direction. The rotation of the plane of polarization by asymmetric molecules is referred to as *optical activity,* and the pair of related molecules are referred to as *optical isomers.*

Optical isomerism is extremely important in the chemistry of living things. Many of the substances that are essential to the diet are optically active. If the organism is fed one of the isomers, it will grow and multiply, whereas it cannot utilize the mirror image at all.

Suggestions for Further Reading

L. Pauling, R. B. Corey, and R. Hayward, "The Structure of Protein Molecules," *Scientific American,* July 1954, p. 51.

P. W. Bridgman, "Synthetic Diamonds," *Scientific American,* Nov. 1955, p. 42.

H. F. Mark, "Giant Molecules," *Scientific American,* Sept. 1957, p. 80.

P. J. W. Debye, "How Giant Molecules are Measured," *Scientific American,* Sept. 1957, p. 90.

J. E. Leffler, *A Short Course in Organic Chemistry* (New York: Macmillan Company, 1959).

H. Hart and R. C. Schuetz, *Organic Chemistry* (New York: Houghton Mifflin Company, 1953).

15 *Reactions of*

Covalent Molecules

IN CHAPTER 3 we discussed the macroscopic characteristics of chemical
change: the reactants which are present initially disappear, while at the
same time the products, a new set of substances with completely different
properties, appear. The chemical reaction is accompanied by the absorption or release of energy. The speeds at which reactions occur vary widely.
A few reactions go to completion in a fraction of a second, perhaps with
explosive violence; many others take minutes, days, or even months to go
to completion. Still others do not go to completion at all, but approach a
final equilibrium state in which both reactants and products are present in
significant amounts. In such an equilibrium state the reactants continue to
be transformed into products, but at the same time the products react to

form the original reactants, and these two processes occur at equal rates. It is also possible for two or more *different* reactions to take place simultaneously when a given set of reactants is mixed. In such a case, the relative amounts of the different products can be changed by changing the reaction conditions.

In this chapter we shall study the theory of the reactions of covalent molecules and learn some of the more important classes of reactions. We shall consider the following questions: What is the nature of the intermediate steps involved in the reaction? Is it necessary that *all* of the covalent bonds in the reactant molecules first be broken before the product molecules can be formed, or are the changes limited to just a few of the covalent bonds? What are the factors that determine the rates of chemical reactions, the positions of chemical equilibria, and the nature of the products? Knowledge of these factors enables the chemist to exercise a certain amount of control over the outcome of his reactions.

Reaction Mechanisms

A reaction mechanism is the series of submicroscopic events whereby reactant molecules are converted to product molecules. We now wish to demonstrate an important feature which is common to all reaction mechanisms: the formation of the product molecules from the reactant molecules must of necessity proceed through some intermediate state or states which are unstable because the octet rule is violated.

We have seen that a covalent molecule is a unit with a definite structure in which the atoms are held together firmly by covalent bonds. When such a molecule reacts to form a new molecule, one or several of the original bonds must be broken and new bonds formed. Consider, for example, the reaction of methyl iodide gas (CH_3I) with hydrogen iodide gas (HI) to produce methane (CH_4) and iodine (I_2):

$$H-\underset{\underset{H}{|}}{\overset{\overset{H}{|}}{C}}-\bar{\underline{I}}\,| \quad + \quad |\bar{I}-H \quad \longrightarrow \quad H-\underset{\underset{H}{|}}{\overset{\overset{H}{|}}{C}}-H \quad + \quad |\bar{\underline{I}}-\bar{\underline{I}}\,|$$

This reaction involves the replacement in the reactant molecules of a C—I bond and an H—I bond by a C—H bond and an I—I bond. We may now use our imaginations and speculate how this reshuffling of bonds might be accomplished. For example, we might propose an initial scission of the old bonds, followed by combination of the fragments in a new arrangement. This sequence of events is shown in equations (1) to (4).

Equation (1): The C—I bond breaks to form two unstable fragments in which the octet rule is violated.

$$\begin{array}{ccccc} \text{H} & & & \text{H} & \\ | & & & | & \\ \text{H}-\text{C}+\bar{\text{I}}| & \longrightarrow & \text{H}-\text{C}□ & + & □\bar{\text{I}}| \\ | & & & | & \\ \text{H} & & & \text{H} & \end{array} \qquad (1)$$

Equation (2): The H—I bond breaks to form two unstable fragments in which the octet rule is violated.

$$\text{H}-\bar{\text{I}}| \longrightarrow \text{H}□ + □\bar{\text{I}}| \qquad (2)$$

Equations (3) and (4): The unstable fragments combine to form stable molecules of methane and iodine.*

$$\begin{array}{ccccc} \text{H} & & & \text{H} & \\ | & & & | & \\ \text{H}-\text{C}□ & + & □\text{H} & \longrightarrow & \text{H}-\text{C}-\text{H} \\ | & & & | & \\ \text{H} & & & \text{H} & \end{array} \qquad (3)$$

$$|\bar{\text{I}}□ + □\bar{\text{I}}| \longrightarrow |\bar{\text{I}}-\bar{\text{I}}| \qquad (4)$$

Since we are merely speculating about the mechanism of this reaction, we are free to consider other possibilities. Thus, we might propose that the new bonds are being formed while the old bonds are still in the process of being broken rather than after the scission is complete. This mechanism is shown in equations (5) and (6).

Equation (5): The molecules of methyl iodide and hydrogen iodide combine to form an unstable intermediate molecule in which the bonds indicated by dotted lines are different from ordinary shared electron-pair bonds.

$$\begin{array}{ccccc} \text{H} & & & \text{H} & |\bar{\text{I}}| \\ | & & & \diagdown & \\ \text{H}-\text{C}-\bar{\text{I}}| & + & \text{H}-\bar{\text{I}}| & \longrightarrow & \text{H}-\text{C} \quad \text{I}| \\ | & & & \diagup \diagdown & \\ \text{H} & & & \text{H} \quad \text{H} & \end{array} \qquad (5)$$

Equation (6): The intermediate molecule breaks up to form methane and iodine.

$$\begin{array}{ccccc} \text{H} & \backslash |\bar{\text{I}}| & & \text{H} & \\ | & \times & & | & \\ \text{H}-\text{C} \backslash \quad \text{I}| & \longrightarrow & \text{H}-\text{C}-\text{H} & + & |\bar{\text{I}}-\bar{\text{I}}| \\ \diagup \quad \backslash & & | & & \\ \text{H} \quad \text{H} \backslash & & \text{H} & \end{array} \qquad (6)$$

---

* The reader should note that the possibility also exists that the unstable fragments combine to re-form the original molecules.

Which, if either, of these two mechanisms is the correct one is something that can be decided only by experiment. Moreover, the particular mechanism that operates may very well change as the reaction conditions are changed. For the purposes of this discussion, the important thing to notice about both mechanisms is that the atoms must momentarily exist in unstable combinations before the product molecules are formed.

The present example is typical of all reactions involving covalent molecules: the replacement of an existing bond by a new bond always proceeds through intermediate states in which the octet rule is violated, and the intermediate states have a high energy content.

This, incidentally, raises another question: From where does this additional energy come? While the average energy of the molecules may be insufficient to form the required intermediate molecules of high energy, there is in any collection of molecules always a small fraction with energies far above the average (Chatper 6, pages 69–71). It is these molecules that, at any given instant, are capable of undergoing reaction. This supply of highly energetic reactant molecules is constantly being replenished. As collisions occur, some molecules acquire energies above the average value at the expense of others, which consequently have energies below the average.

Selectivity of Reagents and the Principle of Minimum Structural Change

Even though covalent bonds are quite strong, there are important differences in the actual strength of different types of covalent bonds. These differences lead to a degree of *selectivity* in the reactions which the compound will undergo, since that reaction is favored in which the weakest bond is broken. Consider, for example, the decomposition of ethylene diiodide by heat.

$$\begin{array}{cc} \text{H} & \text{H} \\ | & | \\ \text{H}-\text{C}-\text{C}-\text{H} \\ | & | \\ |\text{I}| & |\text{I}| \end{array}$$

ethylene diiodide

Which of the bonds, C—H, C—C, or C—I, will be broken? Examination of the table of bond energies (page 184) shows that the carbon-iodine bond is the weakest of the three.

We would therefore expect that when the compound is heated sufficiently, it is the carbon-iodine bonds that break. This is borne out by experiment. The reaction which occurs is shown in equation (7).

TABLE OF BOND ENERGIES

Bond	Bond energy (in calories per mole)
C—C	80,000
C—H	98,200
C—I	56,500
C—Br	65,000
C—Cl	78,000
O—H	109,400
C—O	79,000
H—I	70,600
I—I	35,600

$$
\underset{\text{ethylene diiodide}}{H-\overset{\overset{|\bar{I}|}{|}}{\underset{H}{\overset{|}{C}}}-\overset{\overset{|\bar{I}|}{|}}{\underset{H}{\overset{|}{C}}}-H} \xrightarrow{\text{heat}} \underset{\text{ethylene}}{H-\underset{H}{\overset{|}{C}}=\underset{H}{\overset{|}{C}}-H} + \underset{\text{iodine}}{|\underline{\bar{I}-\bar{I}}|} \qquad (7)
$$

It must not be inferred, however, that bond strength is the only criterion for deciding which bond will break, since most reactions involve a mechanism in which the new bond or bonds are forming while the old bond or bonds are breaking. Thus, the particular reaction which takes place depends not only on the strength of the bond that is breaking, but also on the strength of the newly forming bond. It requires energy to break the old bond, and energy is released when the new bond forms. If the two processes take place simultaneously, then some of the energy released in the formation of the new bond is used to help break the old bond.

If the energy released in forming the new bond is great enough, then some bond other than the weakest may be broken. Thus, instead of each reagent having the same effect, namely, that of breaking the weakest bond, different reagents will attack different bonds in a given molecule.* In other words, reagents are specialists, and each attacks only certain types of bonds, but not others.

Consider, for example, the reaction which ensues when ethyl bromide is added to a solution of the ionic compound, sodium hydroxide. The reaction product is found to be ethyl alcohol, and the reaction is represented by equation (8).

---

* The term "reagent" is used here to denote an attacking molecule or ion.

$$\text{ethyl bromide} \quad \text{hydroxide ion from} \quad \text{ethyl alcohol} \quad \text{bromide ion forms}$$
$$\text{sodium hydroxide} \quad \quad \text{sodium bromide}$$

Comparison of the structural formulas of ethyl alcohol and ethyl bromide

reveals the fact that the H—C—C part of the molecule is unchanged. The

only bond which has been attacked is the C—Br bond, resulting in the replacement of bromine by hydroxyl.

Not infrequently the reaction zone consists of several adjacent bonds or atoms. For example, consider the reaction of the rather complicated molecule of the insecticide, D.D.T., with sodium hydroxide, which is shown in equation (9).

In this reaction two bonds are broken as a result of the attack by the hydroxide ion, a C—H bond and a C—Cl bond, resulting in the formation of a carbon-carbon double bond.

The selectivity of a particular reagent for a given type of bond leads to the *principle of minimum structural change.* According to this principle, a reagent will attack only one bond, or at most a small number of bonds, in the original molecule, leading to a product molecule in which much of the original structure is still intact. This principle makes it possible to predict the molecular structure of the product even for reactions involving very complicated molecules, since only a small portion of the original molecule is altered.

Some Important Types of Reactions

Although myriads of reactions are known involving covalent molecules, it is possible to group these reactions into a few broad classifications. Some of the more important of these classifications will be considered in this section.

The substitution reaction

In this reaction, one atom or group of atoms in the molecule is replaced by another atom or group of atoms. The net result is the breaking of one covalent bond and the formation of a new one in its place. The following reactions are typical substitution reactions:

1. The reaction of ethyl bromide with hydroxide ion; this reaction was discussed on page 185 and is shown in equation (8).
2. The bromination of benzene to form bromobenzene.

$$|\overline{Br}-\overline{Br}| \quad + \qquad\qquad\qquad \longrightarrow \qquad\qquad\qquad + \quad H-\overline{Br}| \quad (10)$$

benzene, C_6H_6 bromobenzene, C_6H_5Br

The decomposition reaction

The decomposition of a covalent molecule involves its breakdown into two or more smaller molecules or into atoms. Usually this is accomplished by heating the substance. As the temperature is raised, the fraction of molecules with energy sufficient to undergo bond rupture becomes appreciable. Even at ordinary temperatures, the atoms in a molecule are vibrating with respect to one another. As the energy of the molecule increases, the violence of these vibrations becomes sufficient to cause the weakest bond to rupture. This phenomenon is depicted in Figure 15-1 for a diatomic molecule. Gaseous bromine at elevated temperatures breaks up into the free atoms.

$$|\overline{Br}-\overline{Br}| \xrightarrow{\text{heat}} 2\ |\overline{Br}\,{}^{\bullet}| \tag{11}$$

Dinitrogen tetroxide (N_2O_4) on heating dissociates into two molecules of nitrogen dioxide (NO_2).

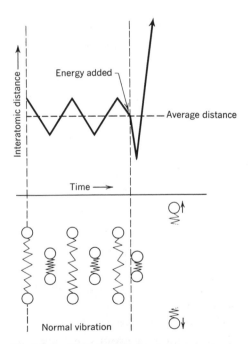

dinitrogen
tetroxide

nitrogen dioxide

$$\tag{12}$$

Fig. 15-1. Bond rupture due to increased amplitude of vibration caused by addition of energy.

Other decomposition reactions are more complicated. For example, when phosphorus pentachloride is heated, it decomposes to give phosphorus trichloride and chlorine.

$$
\underset{\substack{\text{phosphorus}\\\text{pentachloride}}}{\text{(PCl}_5\text{)}} \longrightarrow |\overline{Cl}-\overline{Cl}| \ + \ \underset{\substack{\text{phosphorus}\\\text{trichloride}}}{\text{(PCl}_3\text{)}} \tag{13}
$$

When *iso*-propyl alcohol is passed through a hot tube containing solid aluminum oxide, the products are propylene and water.

$$
\underset{\text{\it iso-propyl alcohol}}{\text{H}-\text{C}-\text{C}-\text{C}-\text{H}} \longrightarrow \underset{\text{propylene}}{\text{H}-\text{C}-\text{C}=\text{C}-\text{H}} \ + \ \text{H}-\overline{\text{O}}-\text{H} \tag{14}
$$

A commercially important decomposition reaction is the "cracking" of long-chain hydrocarbons to produce smaller molecules suitable for use as motor fuel.

Several of the preceding examples are sometimes referred to as *elimination reactions* rather than decomposition. An elimination reaction generally produces a double or triple bond by the removal of atoms or groups from adjacent sites in the molecule. For example, in the decomposition of *iso*-propyl alcohol, a hydroxyl group and a hydrogen atom are detached from adjacent carbon atoms.

The result is that a water molecule is formed, and the C—C single bond becomes a C=C double bond.

Frequently the elimination is assisted by the presence of a reagent which combines with the atoms or groups that are eliminated. Thus 1,2-dichloroethylene is converted to acetylene in the presence of metallic zinc.

$$|\overline{Cl}|\diagdown \quad \diagup H$$

$$C=C \qquad + \quad Zn \quad \longrightarrow \quad H-C\equiv C-H \quad + \quad ZnCl_2 \qquad (15)$$

$$H\diagup \quad \diagdown |\overline{Cl}|$$

trans-1,2-dichloroethylene   acetylene   zinc chloride

Zinc combines with the chlorine atoms to form zinc chloride.

The addition reaction

This type of reaction can be regarded as a reversal of the elimination reaction. Two atoms or groups of atoms are added to adjacent sites in a molecule containing a double or a triple bond. For example, ethylene reacts with bromine to form ethylene dibromide.

$$H-\overset{\displaystyle H}{\underset{\displaystyle |}{C}}=\overset{\displaystyle H}{\underset{\displaystyle |}{C}}-H \quad + \quad |\overline{Br}-\overline{Br}| \quad \longrightarrow \quad H-\overset{\displaystyle H}{\underset{\displaystyle |\overline{Br}|}{C}}-\overset{\displaystyle H}{\underset{\displaystyle |\overline{Br}|}{C}}-H \qquad (16)$$

ethylene dibromide

Two bromine atoms add to the adjacent carbon atoms, thus converting the double bond into a single bond.

Rearrangement

The conversion of one structural isomer into another is referred to as a *rearrangement reaction*. For example, *normal*-butane is converted to its structural isomer, *iso*-butane, in the presence of a catalyst, aluminum chloride.

$$H-\overset{\displaystyle H}{\underset{\displaystyle H}{C}}-\overset{\displaystyle H}{\underset{\displaystyle H}{C}}-\overset{\displaystyle H}{\underset{\displaystyle H}{C}}-\overset{\displaystyle H}{\underset{\displaystyle H}{C}}-H \quad \xrightarrow[\text{catalyst}]{AlCl_3} \quad H-\overset{\displaystyle H}{\underset{\displaystyle H}{C}}-\overset{\overset{\displaystyle H-C-H}{\displaystyle |}}{\underset{\displaystyle H}{C}}-\overset{\displaystyle H}{\underset{\displaystyle H}{C}}-H \qquad (17)$$

normal-butane   *iso*-butane

Another example, which involves an even more extensive rearrangement of the original molecule, is the conversion of *neo*-pentyl alcohol to *tertiary*-amyl alcohol in the presence of an acid.

$$\begin{array}{c}
\text{H} \\
| \\
\text{H-C-H} \\
\text{H} \quad | \quad \text{H} \\
| \quad | \quad | \\
\text{H}-\text{C}-\text{C}-\text{C}-\overline{\text{O}}-\text{H} \\
| \quad | \quad | \\
\text{H} \quad | \quad \text{H} \\
\text{H-C-H} \\
| \\
\text{H}
\end{array}
\quad \xrightarrow{\text{acid}} \quad
\begin{array}{c}
\text{H} \\
| \\
\text{H-C-H} \\
\text{H} \quad | \quad \text{H} \quad \text{H} \\
| \quad | \quad | \quad | \\
\text{H}-\text{C}-\text{C}-\text{C}-\text{C}-\text{H} \\
| \quad | \quad | \quad | \\
\text{H} \; |\text{O}| \; \text{H} \quad \text{H} \\
| \\
\text{H}
\end{array}
\qquad (18)$$

neo-pentyl alcohol   *tertiary-amyl alcohol*

The net result of this rearrangement is that a CH_3 group and an OH group have exchanged places.

Chain reactions

Chlorine molecules, when irradiated with ultraviolet light, absorb· enough energy to break the chlorine-chlorine bond. When chlorine is irradiated in the presence of methane, the chlorine atoms thus produced will attack the C—H bond, forming HCl and ejecting the methyl group. These reactions are shown in equations (19) and (20).

Dissociation of chlorine:

$$|\overline{\text{Cl}}-\overline{\text{Cl}}| \quad \longrightarrow \quad 2\,|\overline{\text{Cl}}\,| \qquad (19)$$

Substitution of Cl for CH_3:

$$|\overline{\text{Cl}}\,| \;+\; \text{H}-\overset{\displaystyle \text{H}}{\underset{\displaystyle \text{H}}{\text{C}}}-\text{H} \quad \longrightarrow \quad |\overline{\text{Cl}}-\text{H} \;+\; \overset{\displaystyle \text{H}}{\underset{\displaystyle \text{H}}{\text{C}}}-\text{H} \qquad (20)$$

The methyl molecule (CH_3) is unstable since it has a half-filled orbital, and will attack another molecule of chlorine, producing a molecule of methyl choride and another free chlorine atom.

$$\text{H}-\overset{\displaystyle \text{H}}{\underset{\displaystyle \text{H}}{\text{C}}} \;+\; |\overline{\text{Cl}}-\overline{\text{Cl}}| \quad \longrightarrow \quad \text{H}-\overset{\displaystyle \text{H}}{\underset{\displaystyle \text{H}}{\text{C}}}-\overline{\text{Cl}}| \;+\; \overline{\text{Cl}}| \qquad (21)$$

The chlorine atom thus produced can attack another methane molecule, as seen in equation (20). This reaction leads to the formation of yet another methyl radical capable of repeating the cycle represented in equations (21) and (20). It has been found that the decomposition of one molecule of chlorine by radiant energy will trigger as many as ten thousand cycles; that is, ten thousand molecules of methyl chloride and of hydrogen chloride are produced as a result of the initial splitting of a single chlorine molecule. A series of reactions of this type, where some outside agency initiates a reaction which then repeats itself again and again, is called a "chain reaction."

The foregoing examples represent a few of the reactions to be found in each of the major classifications. They involve relatively simple molecules, but the reader should realize that the same reactions will occur also with vastly more complicated molecules. Furthermore, several of these reactions may be going on simultaneously in the same reaction mixture. When isopropyl bromide is treated with hydroxide ion, for example, both elimination and substitution occur. This results in a mixture of products.

$$
\begin{array}{c}
& \text{elimination} \\
& \xrightarrow{\hspace{1cm}} \quad
\begin{array}{ccc}
H & H & H \\
| & | & | \\
H-C-C=C-H \\
| \\
H
\end{array}
\quad (22) \\
& \text{propylene}
\end{array}
$$

$$
\begin{array}{ccc}
H & H & H \\
| & | & | \\
H-C-C-C-H \\
| & | & | \\
H & |Br| & H
\end{array}
\quad
\xrightarrow[\text{ion}]{\text{hydroxide}}
$$

iso-propyl bromide

$$
\begin{array}{c}
& \text{substitution} \\
& \xrightarrow{\hspace{1cm}} \quad
\begin{array}{ccc}
H & H & H \\
| & | & | \\
H-C-C-C-H \\
| & | & | \\
H & |O| & H \\
& | \\
& H
\end{array}
\quad (23) \\
& \text{iso-propyl alcohol}
\end{array}
$$

The relative proportion of the products depends on the reaction conditions.

Some Macroscopic Observations Concerning the Speed of Chemical Reactions

Reactions of covalent molecules require anywhere from a fraction of a second to days to be completed. For any specific reaction, the time required depends on the conditions under which the reaction is carried out. The various factors which can influence the rate at which a reaction proceeds will now be considered.

In planning the conditions for carrying out a reaction, the chemist tries to adjust matters so that the reaction is neither explosively fast nor inconveniently slow. He also tries to find conditions under which the desired product is isolated in good yield and in a high state of purity; that is, conditions under which the desired reaction goes virtually to completion and little of the reagents are wasted owing to the formation of undesired by-products.

Perhaps the most important controllable factor is the *reaction temperature*. Almost without exception, an increase in temperature results in acceleration of the reaction, and in many cases the acceleration is very marked. Thus, by carrying out the reaction in an ice bath instead of at room temperature, the reaction may often be slowed down to one-tenth of its original speed, and by raising the temperature to $100°C$, the rate may quite possibly increase a hundred-fold.

Another important factor is the *concentration* of the reactants. The concentration is a measure of the number of molecules in unit volume and is usually expressed in moles (gram molecular weights) per liter. In the gas phase, the concentration of molecules is greater, the greater the pressure (see Chapter 6). In the liquid phase, the concentration of a substance may be varied by dissolving more or less of it in a given amount of solvent. In both cases an increase in the concentration of the reactants frequently results in an increased rate of reaction.

Still another way of changing the rate of a reaction is to carry out the reaction in the presence of a catalyst, a substance that takes part in the reaction and thereby accelerates it without, however, changing the nature of the products.

The magnitude of these factors is best illustrated by some numerical data. First, let us consider the reaction between methyl iodide gas (CH_3I) and hydrogen iodide gas (HI), to produce methane (CH_4) and iodine (I_2):

$$CH_3I + HI \longrightarrow CH_4 + I_2 \tag{24}$$

For this reaction, it is possible to vary the initial concentrations of the two reactants as well as the reaction temperature.

In order to convey an idea of the speed of this reaction as one varies the temperature and the concentration, it is convenient to record the half-reaction time, that is, the time required for one-half of the original reactants to disappear. The results are as shown in the table.

INITIAL CONCENTRATION		Reaction	Half-reaction
CH_3I	HI	temperature	time (calculated)
	(a) Effect of changing the temperature		
0.1 mole/liter	0.1 mole/liter	100°C	7.3 yr
0.1 mole/liter	0.1 mole/liter	200°C	280 min
0.1 mole/liter	0.1 mole/liter	300°C	34 sec
	(b) Effect of changing the concentration		
0.01 mole/liter	0.01 mole/liter	300°C	340 sec
0.1 mole/liter	0.1 mole/liter	300°C	34 sec
1 mole/liter	1 mole/liter	300°C	3.4 sec

Examination of part (a) of the table reveals a dramatic decrease in the half-reaction time as the temperature increases. While at 100°C the reaction is much too slow to be of practical value, requiring years to go to completion, at 300°C the reaction proceeds at quite a convenient rate. The reaction is also speeded up by increasing the concentrations of the reactants, as shown in part (b) of the table, although this effect is not nearly so marked.

The preceding reaction involves the interaction of two different kinds of molecules, CH_3I and HI. It is also of interest to examine a reaction which involves the breakdown of a single molecular species, such as a decomposition reaction. An example is furnished by the decomposition of gaseous *iso*-propyl bromide (C_3H_7Br) into propylene gas (C_3H_6) and hydrogen bromide gas (HBr).

$$\text{(25)}$$

iso-propyl bromide   propylene   hydrogen bromide

Some experimental data obtained for this reaction are shown in the following table.

Initial concentration of C_3H_7Br	Reaction temperature	Half-reaction time (calculated)
	(a) Effect of changing the temperature	
0.1 mole/liter	200°C	6.6 yr
0.1 mole/liter	300°C	8.2 hr
	(b) Effect of changing the concentration	
0.001 mole/liter	300°C	8.2 hr
0.01 mole/liter	300°C	8.2 hr
0.1 mole/liter	300°C	8.2 hr

Again there is a marked increase in the speed of the reaction as the temperature is raised, but the half-reaction time is now independent of the initial concentration.

Another way in which the speed of a reaction can be changed is by the addition of a *catalyst*. The speeding up of reactions by catalysts is of great practical importance. For example, a possible process for the manufacture of sulfuric acid involves the reaction of sulfur dioxide (SO_2) with oxygen (O_2) to form sulfur trioxide (SO_3). The latter subsequently reacts with water to form sulfuric acid.

$$O_2 + 2SO_2 \longrightarrow 2SO_3 \tag{26}$$

$$SO_3 + H_2O \longrightarrow H_2SO_4 \tag{27}$$

Ordinarily, reaction (26) is inconveniently slow. However, the reaction is speeded up by the addition of nitric oxide (NO). A possible interpretation is that nitric oxide reacts rapidly with oxygen to form nitrogen dioxide (NO_2), which in turn reacts rapidly with sulfur dioxide to form the desired sulfur trioxide:

$$O_2 + 2NO \longrightarrow 2NO_2 \tag{28}$$

$$NO_2 + SO_2 \longrightarrow SO_3 + NO \tag{29}$$

Furthermore, as a result of reaction (29), the nitric oxide is regenerated and can repeat its catalytic action. An overall increase in the rate of the reaction is thus achieved by substituting two fast reactions (28 and 29) for one slow one (26).

Another device for speeding up a reaction is to add a *surface catalyst*. This is a solid on the surface of which the reactants are adsorbed in such a way that they are more ready to react than they would be in the absence of the solid. For example, the decomposition of *iso*-propyl alcohol to propylene and water [equation (14)] takes place much more readily in the presence of solid aluminum oxide than in its absence.

Surface catalysis is a highly specific phenomenon. Starting with a given set of reactants, different catalysts can accelerate different reactions leading to different products. Thus, if copper is used instead of aluminum oxide, *iso*-propyl alcohol does not decompose to propylene and water but decomposes in a completely different manner to form acetone (C_3H_6O) and hydrogen.

$$\underset{\substack{\text{H} \quad \text{H} \quad \text{H} \\ | \quad | \quad | \\ \text{H} \quad |\text{O}| \quad \text{H} \\ | \\ \text{H}}}{\text{H}-\overset{|}{\underset{|}{\text{C}}}-\overset{|}{\underset{|}{\text{C}}}-\overset{|}{\underset{|}{\text{C}}}-\text{H}} \quad \xrightarrow[\text{220–270°C}]{\text{copper catalyst}} \quad \underset{\substack{\text{H} \quad |\text{O}| \quad \text{H} \\ | \quad \| \quad | \\ \text{H} \quad \text{H}}}{\text{H}-\overset{|}{\underset{|}{\text{C}}}-\overset{\|}{\underset{}{\text{C}}}-\overset{|}{\underset{|}{\text{C}}}-\text{H}} \quad + \quad \text{H}-\text{H} \qquad (30)$$

acetone

This example illustrates one of the important problems of practical chemistry. The given set of reactants may quite possibly be capable of reacting in different ways to form alternative sets of products. The chemist must then find conditions under which the desired products can be formed so much more rapidly than the undesired ones, that the latter never have a chance to be formed in appreciable amounts.

Theory of Reaction Rates

A theory which explains the effect of temperature, concentration, and catalysts on the rates of reactions in which two or more molecules must come together incorporates three ideas which have been presented earlier in this chapter. According to the theory, the rate of the reaction, that is, the number of molecules reacting in unit time, is equal to the product of the following independent factors:

1. The total number of collisions in unit time;
2. The probability that any given collision will bring the reaction zones of the two reagent molecules into direct contact; and
3. The probability that the colliding molecules have sufficient energy to form the unstable intermediate state of high energy.

We shall now consider how these factors vary with the reaction conditions.

The total number of collisions in unit time

The number of collisions experienced in unit time by a molecule in the gas phase was discussed in Chapter 6 (page 73). It was seen that this number is very large, and that at a given temperature it increases with the pressure, which in turn is a measure of the concentration of the gas molecules. The same rule applies to a mixture of two or more gases. The number of collisions between any two kinds of molecules increases when the concentration of either of the two substances increases. One would therefore expect that the rate of a reaction between the two increases also. The reaction between methyl iodide and hydrogen iodide, discussed on page 192, furnishes a suitable example. An increase in the concentration of the reactants results in an increased reaction rate and a decreased half-reaction time. Many reactions occurring in liquid solutions behave in much the same way.

The number of collisions varies not only with the concentrations of the colliding molecules, but also with the temperature. As the temperature is raised and the average velocity of the molecules increases, collisions become more frequent even though the concentrations remain constant. Hence we would expect an increase in the rate of the reaction. This is again in agreement with observation.

Coincidence of reaction zones

Reaction will occur only in those collisions in which the two reaction zones of the two molecules come in direct contact. Since the reaction zone is normally only a small portion of the total molecule, the odds are strongly against the two reaction zones coinciding. Thus, only a small fraction of all collisions will meet this requirement.

Energy requirement

Just as the boundary of an atom is defined by its outermost electron orbitals, so the boundary of a molecule is defined by the outermost electron orbitals of the molecule. Owing to the rapid motion of the electrons in these orbitals, we may imagine that all atoms and molecules are surrounded by a region of negative charge. This region will act as a defensive barrier against attack by another molecule, since the negative charge will repel the negative charge on the surface of the approaching molecule. In a normal collision this barrier is not penetrated; the molecules come together, collide, and move apart.

In order that reaction may occur, the attacking reagent must penetrate this defensive barrier and come within bond-forming distance of the molecule with which it is to react. This will happen only if the colliding molecules are moving fast enough to overcome the mutual repulsion of their outer boundaries. Moreover, in order for reaction to occur, there must be enough energy so that the relatively unstable configuration of the intermediate state can be attained. For the great majority of reactions, the amount of energy thus required is considerably greater than the kinetic energy possessed by the average molecule.

It has been pointed out (page 70) that only a small fraction of all the molecules will at any given instant possess energy well in excess of the average and therefore be capable of reacting. Of the collisions involving these energetic molecules, only those having the proper alignment of reaction zones will lead to the formation of product molecules. Thus, we must conclude that only a minute fraction of all collisions are effective.

Since the number of highly energetic molecules increases quite sharply with increasing temperature, as shown in Figure 6-2, we would expect that the number of collisions with the required energy also increases quite sharply. As a result, there should be a sharp increase in the rate of the reaction with increasing temperature. This is in agreement with experiment, as shown in the tables on page 193.

Suggestions for Further Reading

E. F. Gale, "Experiments in Protein Synthesis," *Scientific American,* March 1956, p. 42.

J. D. Roberts, "Organic Chemical Reactions," *Scientific American,* Nov. 1957, p. 117.

H. Kalmus, "The Chemical Senses," *Scientific American,* April 1958, p. 97.

G. Natta, "How Giant Molecules are Made," *Scientific American,* Sept. 1957, p. 98.

J. E. Leffler, *A Short Course in Organic Chemistry* (New York: Macmillan Company, 1959).

H. Hart and R. D. Schuetz, *Organic Chemistry* (New York: Houghton Mifflin Company, 1953).

16 *The Atomic Nucleus*

THE EXPERIMENTS of Ernest Rutherford on the scattering of alpha particles by thin foils of metal offered strong evidence for the existence of an atomic nucleus bearing a positive charge of electricity and containing almost the entire mass of the atom. In our discussion of chemical bonding and molecular structure the nucleus played only a minor role, because these phenomena could be discussed fruitfully by considering only the electrons in the outermost shell of the atom. There is, however, a whole range of extremely important phenomena whose understanding depends on a detailed knowledge of the nucleus. In this chapter we shall consider the constitution of the atomic nucleus. We shall discuss its component parts and examine some of the ideas that have been developed concerning its structure.

The Discovery of the Proton

It will be recalled that radioactivity involves the *spontaneous* disintegration of atomic nuclei with the ejection of small particles, such as alpha particles (helium nuclei) or beta particles (electrons). Rutherford, while studying natural radioactivity, became convinced that the disintegration was due to the intrinsic instability of the radioactive nucleus. He then began to speculate on the possibility of bringing about nuclear disintegration by artificial means. In his early experiments, he bombarded the nuclei of certain elements with energetic alpha particles ejected by radioactive atoms in the course of their spontaneous disintegration, thus hoping to cause new nuclear reactions to take place.

The experiment that interests us at this point is the bombardment of nitrogen nuclei with alpha particles. Rutherford found in 1918 that, when nitrogen gas is exposed to a stream of fast-moving alpha particles, every once in a while (about once for every 10,000 alpha particles) the nucleus of a nitrogen atom disappears, and in its place there appears an atom of oxygen and another less heavy particle with a charge of $+1$ and a mass of 1. The reader will recognize that the latter particle is a hydrogen nucleus or *proton*. (This experiment was carried out in a Wilson cloud chamber, the operation of which will be considered shortly.)

This nuclear reaction is of tremendous interest for two reasons. First, and perhaps most startling, is the fact that it represents the artificial *transmutation* of one element into another! Never before in all his tinkering with matter had man been able to transform one element into another. During the Middle Ages the alchemists had as their primary goal the conversion of the base metals into gold, but of course they never succeeded. In all *ordinary chemical reactions* the nucleus of the atom is left unaltered, and therefore the element survives as such throughout the most extensive and complicated of chemical reactions.

The second and more fundamental reason for our interest in this experiment is that the discovery of the proton gives us a clue as to the possible composition of the nucleus. It was later found that this same particle is produced in many other nuclear reactions. It is therefore probable that the proton is one of the fundamental building blocks of the nucleus, in the same way that the electron is one of the fundamental building blocks of the entire atom.

The Discovery of the Neutron

A number of years after Rutherford's discovery of the proton, Chadwick, a former student of Rutherford's, demonstrated the existence of yet another fundamental particle.* In 1930 it was observed that when beryllium was bombarded with alpha particles, there was produced a very penetrating radiation which for a time was thought to be gamma radiation. Chadwick demonstrated, however, that this mysterious radiation was a stream of fast-moving particles of about the same mass as a proton but having no electric charge. Because of their electrical neutrality, these particles were called *neutrons.*

The lack of charge on the neutron is responsible for its great penetrating power. Protons of the same energy are stopped by a much thinner layer of matter because of the interaction of their electric charges with the charges of the nuclei and electrons in the matter they are traversing.

In discussing nuclear particles, it is convenient to introduce the concept of the *mass number* (A). The mass number is defined as the atomic mass of the nuclear particle or nucleus (in atomic weight units), rounded off to the nearest whole number. Thus the mass number of the neutron, as well as that of the proton, is equal to *one.*

The Proton-Neutron Theory of the Nucleus

With the discovery of the proton and the neutron, it became possible to develop a consistent theory of nuclear composition, according to which nuclei are made up of protons and neutrons. Since each proton has a single positive charge, the number of protons in the nucleus of a given element is equal to the total nuclear charge characteristic of that element, which in

---

* By "fundamental particle" is meant a particle that cannot be further broken down into still simpler particles. This definition is reminiscent of our earlier definition of the elements; and in a certain sense, of course, the concept of a small number of fundamental particles replaces the concept of a small number of different kinds of atoms. In this chapter four fundamental particles are mentioned: electrons, protons, neutrons, and mesons. However, within the past few years a large number of other fundamental particles have been discovered; so many, in fact, that the "fundamental" identity of some of them is now under question.

turn is equal to the atomic number (page 100). For example, the element of atomic number 10 has a nuclear charge of $+10$ and therefore contains 10 protons in the nucleus.

However, with the exception of the hydrogen nucleus, the observed masses of all known nuclei are greater than the total mass of the required number of protons. The theory must therefore make provision for adding mass to the nucleus without adding charge. This is done by adding a number of neutrons of unit mass and zero charge. For example, if an atom of atomic number 10 has a mass number of 20, ten neutrons must be added to the 10 protons. In general, the number of neutrons present in the nucleus of any atom is equal to the *difference* between the mass number (A) and the atomic number (Z).

The proton-neutron theory of the nucleus is summarized by the following relationships:

(1)   number of protons = atomic number (Z)
(2)   number of neutrons = mass number (A) − atomic number (Z)

The reader will recall that the number of orbital electrons in the *neutral atom* is equal to the nuclear charge. Therefore we obtain an additional relationship:

(3)   number of orbital electrons = number of protons in nucleus = Z

The application of the proton-neutron theory to a number of different nuclei is illustrated in the table.

Nucleus	Mass number (A)	Atomic number (Z)	No. of protons	No. of neutrons
Hydrogen-1	1	1	1	0
Helium-4	4	2	2	2
Lithium-7	7	3	3	4
Oxygen-16	16	8	8	8
Fluorine-19	19	9	9	10
Gold-197	197	79	79	118
Radon-222	222	86	86	136

For the lighter elements the number of protons and neutrons is about equal, while for the heavy elements the number of neutrons is significantly greater than the number of protons. Since the protons all possess a positive charge, they mutually repel one another. As the number of protons in the nucleus rises, more and more neutrons seem to be required to separate the protons and to reduce their repulsive interaction.

Isotopes

All atoms of the same element have identical nuclear charges, but they need not have identical masses. For ordinary chemical reactions this latter fact rarely ever causes any complications, because the chemical behavior of all the atoms of a given element is very similar, regardless of their masses. Thus, for chemical purposes, it is sufficient to characterize the atoms of the given element by their average atomic weight, which is the mean weight of all the atoms. For example, naturally occurring tin (atomic number 50) is a mixture of atoms with the atomic mass numbers 112, 114, 115, 116, 117, 118, 119, 120, 122, and 124. The mean weight of all the tin atoms in such a sample has been determined by chemical analysis as 118.7. This mean atomic weight can be used in all chemical calculations involving samples of tin derived from natural sources.

In contrast, in a nuclear reaction, the mass numbers of the individual nuclei are important factors. For example, under a given set of conditions uranium atoms of mass 238 and 235 undergo entirely different nuclear reactions. It is therefore important to specify not only the element, but also the mass number of the *isotope* involved in the reaction.*

The two isotopes of uranium mentioned above can be represented as follows:

$$\text{uranium-235} = {}_{92}U^{235}$$
$$\text{uranium-238} = {}_{92}U^{238}$$

In this representation, the nuclear charge (Z) is shown as a subscript preceding the symbol of the element, and the nuclear mass (A) is shown as a superscript following the symbol. Thus, for the general case we have, $_Z\text{symbol}^A$.

Particles encountered in nuclear reactions may also be symbolized in this way. Some examples are shown in the following table.

Common name	Symbol	Mass number (A)	Charge (Z)	Remarks
Alpha particle	${}_2He^4$	4	2	helium nucleus
Beta particle	${}_{-1}e^0$	0	−1	electron
Proton	${}_1H^1$	1	1	hydrogen nucleus
Deuteron	${}_1H^2$	2	1	heavy hydrogen nucleus
Neutron	${}_0n^1$	1	0	—————

* Derived from the Greek words *iso* and *topos,* meaning "same place," and refers to atoms belonging to the same space in the periodic table. The atoms differ only in their atomic mass.

The existence of isotopes is readily understood in terms of the proton-neutron theory of the nucleus. The nuclei of different isotopes of the same element all have the same number of protons but different numbers of neutrons. Thus, $_{92}U^{235}$ has 92 protons and 143 neutrons, while $_{92}U^{238}$ has 92 protons and 146 neutrons.

By means which will be discussed in the next chapter, it has been possible to prepare a large number of artificial isotopes, so that today the 102 chemical elements exhibit over 1000 different isotopic forms. Many of these new isotopes have found widespread use as "tracers" in medicine, industry, agriculture, and in other branches of science.

The Detection of Nuclear Particles

In order to study the nature of nuclear reactions such as those which led to the discovery of the proton and the neutron, it was necessary to develop techniques for the detection and characterization of nuclear particles. These techniques are different from those employed to identify the products of *chemical* reactions. In contrast to chemical reactions, where one obtains huge numbers of product molecules which can be separated by macroscopic procedures, in nuclear reactions one often attempts to detect individual particles or events. When one considers that *whole* atoms are much too small to be visible, the detection of *nuclear* particles whose dimensions are of the order of 1/10,000 of those of atoms must seem like an insurmountable task. Nevertheless, a variety of ingenious methods have been devised. One of these methods, the use of a scintillating screen, was discussed in connection with Rutherford's alpha scattering experiments (page 97). There are other methods for detecting nuclear particles, some of which will even render visible the actual nuclear reactions that take place.

Photographic film

The initial (and accidental) discovery of radioactivity by Becquerel in 1895 depended upon the effect such particles as protons, electrons, alpha particles, and gamma rays have on a piece of photographic film. In connection with some other experiments, the French scientist had left a crystal of a uranium salt in contact with a photographic plate which was wrapped in thick black paper. Through one of those coincidences which play an important role in scientific discoveries, Becquerel developed this plate and found, much to his amazement, an image of the crystal imprinted on the plate. Evidently the uranium was emitting some invisible and penetrating radiation or particle which was capable of affecting the photographic plate in the same manner as ordinary light, but which could pass through the paper in which the plate was wrapped. This photographic technique has been refined and extended, and is widely used today in many investigations in nuclear physics. It has the obvious advantage of producing a permanent record of the passage of the nuclear particle which can be studied at leisure. Much of our knowledge, for example, of cosmic rays has come from the study of photographic plates that have been carried to high altitudes by balloons where they are exposed to the bombardment of these mysterious particles or radiations from outer space. A more mundane application is found in the so-called "film badge," which is simply a piece of film in an opaque case worn by scientists who work in the vicinity of sources of this type of radiation. Development of the film reveals the amount of radiation received by the wearer, by measurement of the amount of blackening that the film has undergone.

The Wilson cloud chamber

Earlier in this chapter the transmutation of a nitrogen atom into an oxygen atom with the accompanying production of a proton was discussed. The ingenious method whereby these events, involving the nuclei of *single*

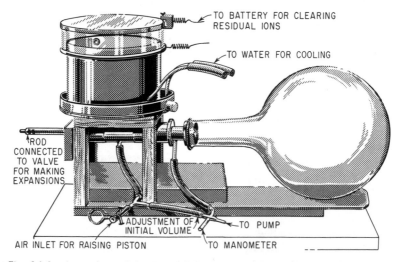

Fig. 16-1. An early model (1911) of the Wilson cloud chamber. The tracks are generated in the cylindrical chamber at the top of the apparatus. After a photograph by P. M. S. Blackett, from *Les Inventeurs Celebres* (Paris: Mazenod, 1950).

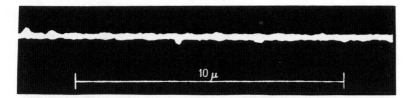

Fig. 16-2. Cloud chamber track of a slow proton.

atoms, were made visible and studied deserves consideration since it has been one of the most fruitful techniques for the study of nuclear properties and nuclear reactions. The device employed is called the "Wilson cloud chamber" after its inventor, C. T. R. Wilson. The manner in which the cloud chamber depicts the path of nuclear particles is in many ways analogous to the way in which vapor trails indicate the path of high-flying aircraft. Frequently these aircraft are flying at such great altitudes as to be themselves invisible, but their passage is made quite evident by the "trail" which they leave behind them. In a similar fashion, while the particle itself is not made visible in the cloud chamber, its passage is clearly marked by a "fog trail" which it leaves in its wake.

The air within the cloud chamber contains an excess of water vapor, but condensation to form a cloud does not occur under ordinary conditions because the water molecules must have some kind of centers (called condensation nuclei) around which to collect into droplets visible to the eye. Now, if a fast-moving particle like a proton or nitrogen nucleus passes through this water-laden air, it produces a wake of *ions.* These ions are formed from the nitrogen and oxygen molecules of which the air is composed by the "knocking out" of electrons by the swiftly moving nuclear particle. The ions are ideal "condensation nuclei," and the water condenses on them rapidly to form visible droplets, thus producing a "vapor trail" behind the moving nucleus. In Figures 16-2 and 16-3 are seen vapor trails (or fog tracks) produced by the passage of protons and electrons. It will be noted that the thickness and length of the tracks differ for the different particles.* The track formed by the proton is thicker because the proton produces more ions per unit length of track. These characteristic differences permit identification of the particular particle producing the fog track.

Figure 16-4 is a photograph of the event described by Rutherford. Coming from the bottom of the photograph we see the tracks left by a number of alpha particles. At the point indicated by the arrow, one of them

---

* The Greek letter μ stands for "micron," a unit of length equal to 0.001 mm.

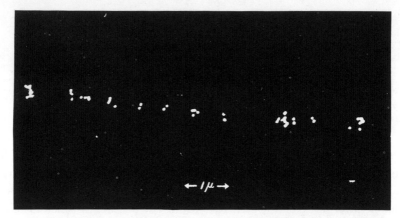

Fig. 16-3. Cloud chamber track of a fast-moving electron.

Fig. 16-4. A cloud chamber picture of alpha tracks in nitrogen. The arrow indicates the site of the nuclear reaction. After a photograph by P. M. S. Blackett.

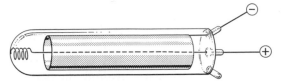

Fig. 16-5. Schematic diagram of a Geiger tube.

has collided with the nucleus of a nitrogen atom; and emanating from this point are two quite different tracks, a short thick one and a longer, less dense one. By the study of many events of this kind and the use of auxiliary apparatus, it can be shown that the short, thick track is indeed one left by an oxygen nucleus, and the longer one is due to a fast-moving proton.

Geiger tubes

Geiger tubes (Figure 16-5) also depend for their operation on the ionizing property of fast-moving, charged nuclear particles. The tube consists of a thin glass envelope through which the nuclear particles can pass. Inside the envelope is a cylinder of metal, down the center of which is suspended a thin wire, which is insulated from the metal cylinder. The tube is filled with a suitable gas (often a mixture of argon and ethyl alcohol vapor), and the wire and metal cylinder are connected to a source of high voltage. Ordinarily, no current flows because of the gap in the circuit owing to the lack of contact between the wire and the metal cylinder. But if a nuclear particle creates a shower of ions in this gap, a brief pulse of electricity is generated as the ions are attracted to the electrodes. This pulse can be amplified and made to activate a device which counts the pulse and records the passage of *each* particle through the detecting tube.

Nuclear Structure

We have already sketched in the simplest possible picture of nuclear structure—a tiny cluster of neutrons and protons at the center of the atom. This picture is of course quite incomplete and raises a great many new questions. For example, what holds the particles together? Are they organized in any particular way, or simply lumped in a random fashion? And are these the only particles to be found within the nucleus? These problems will now be considered briefly.

Nuclear forces

When we examine the characteristics of the force that binds together two protons, or a proton and a neutron, or two neutrons, or the force that binds together the 238 particles that constitute the nucleus of a uranium-238 atom, we quickly discover that this force is quite unlike anything we have encountered previously. Whereas the electrostatic forces which were invoked to explain the formation of molecules or the binding of electrons to the positive nucleus diminish in intensity relatively slowly as the two charged particles are separated, nuclear forces act only over *very* short distances. In fact, if the nuclear particles are separated by distances much greater than the nuclear diameter, the attraction ceases. Furthermore, this force is independent of the charge of the particles; the same force which binds together a neutron and a proton will also bind together two neutrons, or two protons.

The nature of this force is not clear. When the concept of the covalent bond was developed, an attempt was made to extend the same general idea to the field of nuclear binding. This hypothesis implied that, just as two atoms were held together by the sharing of electrons, so could two nuclear particles be held together by the exchange of electrical charge. Unfortunately, as soon as it became possible to make a somewhat accurate estimate of the strength of nuclear forces, this hypothesis became untenable. The force of attraction expected from the exchange of a positive charge between a proton and a neutron is much too weak to be responsible for binding these two particles together.

In 1935, the Japanese physicist, H. Yukawa, suggested that a then undiscovered particle, now called the *meson,* was acting as a nuclear "glue" to bind the nuclear particles together. The role of the meson in Yukawa's

Hideki Yukawa: 1907–

Well-known for his investigations of nuclear binding forces.

theory is reminiscent of the role of the electron in the theory of the covalent bond; that is, the meson is shared by the nuclear particles to produce a binding force. On the basis of this theory, the mass of the meson was predicted to be intermediate between that of the electron and the proton. In support of Yukawa's hypothesis, a number of different particles with a mass in the required range have since been discovered. Therefore this particular theory has been pursued vigorously, but it is still incapable of explaining many of the experimental facts.

It is clear that our understanding of the nature of nuclear binding forces is far from complete. Much research is being done in this area, and we may hope for exciting advances in the future.

Nuclear models

A number of different models have been developed for nuclear structure, just as models have been developed for atomic structure and molecular structure. These nuclear models are, however, not nearly so complete or "sophisticated" as the atomic and molecular models which describe the characteristics of atoms and molecules with considerable precision.

In this connection we shall consider only the "shell" model of the nucleus. According to this model, the nuclear particles are organized in shells, just as the electrons surrounding the nucleus are organized in shells of orbitals. The nucleus may therefore be said to have a definite structure.

The evidence in favor of a shell model for the nucleus is much like that which has led to a shell model of electronic structure. In recent years it has become apparent that many nuclear properties vary periodically in a manner similar to the periodic variation of the elements. Just as the atomic numbers 2, 10, 18, 36, and so on, are associated with elements of unusual stability, so there seem to be certain "magic numbers" of protons or neutrons which produce nuclei that are particularly stable. Thus, if the number of protons, or the number of neutrons, is 2, 8, 20, 50, and so forth, the resulting nucleus will have a relatively low internal energy, and the corresponding isotope will be relatively plentiful in nature. It is found that $_2He^4$ (2 neutrons, 2 protons) and $_8O^{16}$ (8 protons, 8 neutrons) are both much more stable than, for example, $_2He^3$ or $_8O^{17}$. When we look at the natural abundances of the isotopes, we find that definite peaks in abundance occur at the isotopes listed in the table on page 210. Note that each of these isotopes has at least one "magic number" associated with it.

Isotope	Number of protons	Number of neutrons
$_8O^{16}$	8	8
$_{20}Ca^{40}$	20	20
$_{38}Sr^{88}$	38	50
$_{39}Y^{89}$	39	50
$_{40}Zr^{90}$	40	50
$_{50}Sn^{118}$	50	68

The "magic numbers" have been interpreted as representing *filled shells* of neutrons or protons, just as the numbers 2 and 10 (2 + 8) represent filled shells of electrons in atomic structure. The shell model of the nucleus has been quite fruitful in predicting the properties of new isotopes not occurring in nature. Just as the periodic chart of the elements predicted the existence of certain as yet undiscovered elements, so the shell model predicts something of the nature and stability of isotopes that one might hope to prepare by nuclear reactions.

Suggestions for Further Reading

Maria G. Mayer, "The Structure of the Nucleus," *Scientific American,* March 1951, p. 22.

Philip and Emily Morrison, "The Neutron," *Scientific American,* Oct. 1951, p. 44.

H. Yagoda, "The Tracks of Nuclear Particles," *Scientific American,* May 1956, p. 40.

E. Segré and C. E. Wiegand, "The Antiproton," *Scientific American,* June 1956, p. 37.

M. Gell-Mann and E. P. Rosenbaum, "Elementary Particles," *Scientific American,* July 1957, p. 72.

V. F. Weisskopf and E. P. Rosenbaum, "A Model of the Nucleus," *Scientific American,* Dec. 1955, p. 84.

17 *Nuclear Reactions*

and Nuclear Energy

Radioactive Decay as a Nuclear Reaction

Natural radioactivity was first mentioned in Chapter 8 as evidence that the one-piece, indestructible atom envisioned by John Dalton was unsatisfactory. It will be recalled that radioactive decay involves the spontaneous disintegration of the nuclei of certain isotopes, with the emission of an alpha particle or a beta particle and the production of a nucleus of a different element. For example, atoms of thorium-232 are converted spontaneously to atoms of radium-228, with each conversion accompanied by the emission of an alpha particle ($_2He^4$). The radium-228 produced from the decay of thorium-232 is also radioactive and decays with the emission of a beta particle ($_{-1}e^0$) to form radioactive actinium-228. Disintegration

211

continues through a series of steps until finally all of the thorium-232 is converted to lead-208. The process takes a very long time, with half the thorium decaying in a matter of some ten billion years.

There are over 40 naturally occurring radioactive isotopes, most of them of high atomic weight. A few of the more important ones are listed in the table.

Isotope	Particle emitted	Half-life (years)
C^{14}	beta	5.7×10^3
K^{40}	beta	1.4×10^9
Rb^{87}	beta	6×10^{10}
In^{115}	beta	6×10^{14}
Sn^{124}	beta	greater than 1.7×10^{17}
La^{138}	beta	1.2×10^{12}
Re^{187}	beta	4×10^{12}
Ra^{226}	alpha	1.6×10^3
Th^{232}	alpha	1.4×10^{10}
Th^{230}	alpha	8.0×10^4
Pa^{231}	alpha	3.4×10^4
U^{235}	alpha	7.1×10^8
U^{238}	alpha	4.5×10^9

The half-life of a radioactive isotope is a property characteristic of that particular isotope and is equal to the time it takes for half of the original sample to decay. Thus, if an isotope has a half-life of 10 years, half of the original sample will have undergone disintegration at the end of 10 years. After an additional 10 years, or a total of 20 years, half of the remaining half will have decayed, so that a quarter of the original is left ($\frac{1}{2} \times \frac{1}{2} = \frac{1}{4}$). Similarly, after 30 years or three half-lives, one eighth of the original sample remains ($\frac{1}{2} \times \frac{1}{2} \times \frac{1}{2} = \frac{1}{8}$); and so on.

Note that the decay rate is always based on the amount of material *left*. It is important to avoid the erroneous assumption that the entire sample of material will decay in just twice the half-life. The right and the wrong view of radioactive decay are contrasted in Figure 17-1.

The range of half-lives for different radioactive isotopes is enormous, from less than a ten-millionth (10^{-7}) of a second to billions of billions (10^{17}) of years. Under ordinary conditions, the half-lives are independent of the temperature of the sample and of the nature of the "host molecule," that is, the molecule of which the radioactive atom is a part. This property of a fixed and characteristic half-life has been of great usefulness in determining the age of materials containing radioactive atoms. Our best estimates of the age of the earth are based on this concept. Knowing the

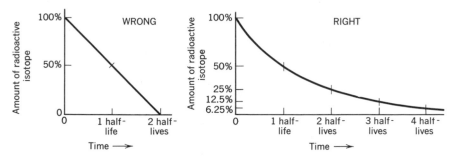

Fig. 17-1. Graphs of the wrong and the right conception of radio-active decay.

half-life of a given radioactive isotope, we need only determine the ratio of parent atoms to decay products in the sample. It is then a simple matter to calculate the amount of time required to reach this ratio, assuming that at the beginning of the process only parent atoms were present. On this basis, the age of the oldest rocks in the earth's crust has been estimated as four billion years.

Alpha Emission

Let us examine the process of radioactive decay in terms of the proton-neutron theory of the nucleus. The first example to be considered is that of an alpha emitter, that is, of a nucleus which decays by the emission of an alpha particle. There are two major questions to be considered: first, what happens to the parent nucleus as a consequence of this emission; and second, why do certain isotopes undergo this type of spontaneous disinte-gration while others do not?

The consequences of alpha emission are best understood by considering a few examples, keeping a close audit on the various nuclear particles involved in the process.

Uranium-238 ($_{92}U^{238}$) is an alpha emitter. The nucleus of $_{92}U^{238}$ consists of 92 protons and 146 neutrons. The alpha particle ($_2He^4$) consists of 2 pro-tons and 2 neutrons. The ejection of an alpha particle is therefore equiva-lent to the loss of 2 protons and 2 neutrons by the uranium-238 nucleus. As a consequence, the "daughter nucleus" consists of 90 protons and 144 neutrons. But such a nucleus is no longer a nucleus of uranium; it is a nucleus of the element thorium, with atomic number 90 and atomic mass 234. These facts are conveniently summarized as follows:

$$\boxed{\begin{array}{c}92\text{ p}\\146\text{ n}\end{array}} \longrightarrow \boxed{\begin{array}{c}2\text{ p}\\2\text{ n}\end{array}} + \boxed{\begin{array}{c}90\text{ p}\\144\text{ n}\end{array}}$$

| uranium-238 | alpha | thorium-234 |
| nucleus | particle | nucleus |

or even more compactly:

$$_{92}U^{238} \longrightarrow {}_2He^4 + {}_{90}Th^{234}$$

Since this is an equation, the amounts involved on both sides of the arrow must balance; that is, the atomic number of the parent must equal the sum of the atomic numbers of the products, and similarly for the mass numbers.

Thorium-234 is also an alpha emitter. Since thorium-234 contains 90 protons, the ejection of an alpha particle will reduce the number of protons to 88. The loss of two neutrons will in a similar fashion reduce the number of neutrons from 144 to 142. The result is the production of a daughter nucleus with a mass number that is four less than that of the parent nucleus, and with a nuclear charge (or atomic number) that is two less, namely the nucleus of a radium atom:

$$\boxed{\begin{array}{c}90\text{ p}\\144\text{ n}\end{array}} \longrightarrow \boxed{\begin{array}{c}2\text{ p}\\2\text{ n}\end{array}} + \boxed{\begin{array}{c}88\text{ p}\\142\text{ n}\end{array}}$$

| thorium-234 | alpha | radium-230 |
| nucleus | particle | nucleus |

or

$$_{90}Th^{234} \longrightarrow {}_2He^4 + {}_{88}Ra^{230}$$

Beta Emission

The case of beta emission is somewhat more complicated, but is still understandable in terms of the proton-neutron theory. A beta particle is the same as an electron; that is, it has negligible mass and bears a single negative charge. The beta particle can therefore be symbolized as $_{-1}e^0$. Electrons *per se* are not present in the nucleus. The fact that they emerge from the nucleus can only mean that they are somehow generated in the nucleus and then ejected immediately. What sort of process could lead to the formation of an electron within the nucleus? A readily envisioned process is the conversion of a neutron ($_0n^1$) to a proton ($_1H^1$) plus an electron, as illustrated in the following equation:

$$_0n^1 \longrightarrow {}_{-1}e^0 + {}_1H^1$$

The charges of the newly-formed particles (-1 and $+1$) add up to zero, and the masses (0 and 1) add up to one. Since these quantities are equal to the charge and mass, respectively, of the neutron, our postulate is satisfactory, at least on a "bookkeeping basis."

Now, if beta emission involves the conversion of a neutron to a proton, then the mass number of the beta-emitting nucleus will not change, but the atomic number (equal to the number of protons in the nucleus) will increase by one. Consider, for example, the case of carbon-14 which is a beta emitter. When a carbon-14 nucleus decays, the daughter nucleus is that of nitrogen-14:

| carbon-14 | beta | nitrogen-14 |
| nucleus | particle | nucleus |

Examination of this schematic representation of the decay process shows that one of the 8 neutrons in the C-14 nucleus has been converted to a proton, giving 7 protons and 7 neutrons in the daughter nucleus, which is therefore nitrogen-14. More briefly, this nuclear change can be represented as:

$$_6C^{14} \longrightarrow {}_{-1}e^0 + {}_7N^{14}$$

In this equation, both the mass numbers and the nuclear charges are balanced, following the same rules as were stated for the case of alpha emission.

Theory of Radioactive Decay for Heavy Atoms

The intriguing question still remains: Why do certain isotopes undergo this spontaneous disintegration? And further, why do some isotopes emit alpha particles, while others are beta emitters?

Rutherford had suggested that radioactive decay was the result of an intrinsic instability of the nuclei of certain isotopes, especially of those of high atomic weight. It appears that, as the aggregate of protons and neutrons becomes larger and larger, the ability of the neutrons to neutralize the repulsion between the positively charged protons is diminished to the point where the nuclear forces are unable to hold this collection of particles together, and pieces of it begin to break off. A particularly stable fragment to break off is the alpha particle. The ejection of such a particle reduces the number of protons in the nucleus and hence the repulsive forces associated with them. If the ejection of one alpha particle does not sufficiently stabilize the nucleus, the process will be repeated until a degree of stability is achieved. However, the act of ejecting alpha particles seems to have an undesirable effect on the ratio of neutrons to protons. Every time an alpha particle is ejected, the ratio of neutrons to protons increases, and after several such events, the ratio may become undesirably high. Such an unstable nucleus can stabilize itself by emitting a beta particle, thus converting a neutron into a proton (see page 214) and reducing the neutron/proton ratio. A sequence of events like this is illustrated by the radioactive series in which radium-223 is converted in a number of steps to the stable isotope, lead-207.

Isotope	Particle ejected	Ratio of neutrons to protons
$_{88}Ra^{223}$		1.53
$\downarrow$	alpha	
$_{86}Rn^{219}$		1.54
$\downarrow$	alpha	
$_{84}Po^{215}$		1.56
$\downarrow$	alpha	
$_{82}Pb^{211}$		1.57
$\downarrow$	**beta**	
$_{83}Bi^{211}$		**1.55**
$\downarrow$	alpha	
$_{81}Tl^{207}$		1.57
$\downarrow$	**beta**	
$_{82}Pb^{207}$		**1.55**

There are a number of other processes whereby radioactive elements may achieve greater stability, such as the emission of a positron (a positively charged particle of electron mass), the capture by the nucleus of an orbital electron that combines with a proton to form a neutron, and the emission of a gamma ray. Space does not permit a detailed discussion of these processes, however.

Determination of Avogadro's number

The development of techniques for the counting of individual alpha particles has provided us with another tool for the direct determination of Avogadro's number, that is, the number of molecules in one gram molecular weight or the number of atoms in one gram atomic weight. Since alpha particles are nuclei of helium atoms, they need only acquire a pair of electrons to become ordinary helium atoms. This happens readily after the alpha particles have slowed down.

One gram of radium is known to emit 4.35×10^{18} alpha particles per year. The British scientists, Ramsay and Soddy, had shown that a gram of radium in one year produces enough alpha particles to form 0.158 cc of helium gas (under standard conditions), or 2.82×10^{-5} g of helium. Thus, 2.82×10^{-5} g of helium consists of 4.35×10^{18} helium atoms. It follows that one gram atomic weight of helium, weighing 4.00 g, consists of $4.00 \times 4.35 \times 10^{18} \div 2.82 \times 10^{-5}$, or 6.16×10^{23} atoms. This value is very close to the most accurate current value for Avogadro's number, 6.023×10^{23} atoms per gram atomic weight.

Artifically Induced Nuclear Reactions

So far we have discussed just one type of nuclear reaction: that which occurs during the disintegration of a naturally radioactive substance. In addition to this type, there are a wide variety of other nuclear reactions which can be brought about by the *bombardment* of nuclei with such sub-atomic particles as protons, alpha particles, neutrons, and electrons, or with gamma rays. These include (1) transmutation to a new stable isotope, (2) transmutation to a new radioactive isotope, (3) nuclear fission, and (4) nuclear fusion. Which of these several reactions occurs depends on: (1) the kind of nucleus being bombarded, (2) the nature of the bombarding particle, and (3) the *energy* of the bombarding particle. In the following sections these various factors will be considered in turn.

In order for an artificially induced nuclear reaction to occur, the target nucleus must be bombarded by some subatomic particle. In all cases except those involving neutrons, electrons, or gamma rays, the bombarding particle has a positive charge. Since the nuclei of atoms are also positively charged, it is obvious that there will be an electrostatic repulsion to be overcome before the bombarding particle (projectile) can enter the target nucleus. This repulsion is overcome by giving the projectile a high velocity and therefore considerable kinetic energy.

In the earliest experiments involving nuclear transformation, the only projectiles available were those ejected during the course of the disintegration of naturally radioactive atoms. Thus Rutherford used the alpha particles ejected by polonium as projectiles in the experiment which resulted in the transformation of nitrogen atoms into oxygen atoms. The limitation inherent in the use of naturally available particles is that their energy is determined by the nature of the radioactive decay process and cannot be varied at will. In order to overcome this limitation and to have available particles of very high kinetic energy, various devices such as the cyclotron, the Van de Graaff accelerator, and the betatron have been invented. The operating principle of all accelerators is the same, although the details of construction and operation vary widely depending on the energy range and the type of particle employed. In every case, because the particle is charged, it can be accelerated by taking advantage of the attractive and repulsive forces that exist between unlike and like charges, respectively.

These attractive and repulsive forces serve to push the particles to high velocities so that, on encountering the target nucleus, they are able to produce the desired nuclear reaction.

Nuclear Transmutation

Using either the naturally available alpha particles, or artificially accelerated alphas, protons, electrons, and so forth, it is possible to carry out a large variety of nuclear reactions leading to both stable and artificially radioactive products. In equations (1) to (4) a number of examples of nuclear transformations are given:

$$_7N^{14} + {}_2He^4 \longrightarrow {}_8O^{17} + {}_1H^1 \tag{1}$$

$$_{13}Al^{27} + {}_2He^4 \longrightarrow {}_{15}P^{30} + {}_0n^1 \tag{2}$$

$$_{11}Na^{23} + {}_1H^1 \longrightarrow {}_{12}Mg^{23} + {}_0n^1 \tag{3}$$

$$_3Li^7 + {}_1H^2 \longrightarrow {}_3Li^8 + {}_1H^1 \tag{4}$$

Equation (1) represents the bombardment of nitrogen-14 atoms with alpha particles and is, of course, the classical experiment of Rutherford. Equation (2) represents the first transmutation leading to the production of a radioactive isotope not found in nature. The reaction was first carried out in 1934 by Irene Joliot-Curie, the daughter of the discoverers of radium and polonium, and her husband, Frédèric Joliot.

Phosphorus-30, the product in equation (2), decays by ejecting a *positron* or positively charged electron, $_{+1}e^0$, as shown in equation (5).

$$_{15}P^{30} \longrightarrow {}_{14}Si^{30} + {}_{+1}e^0 \tag{5}$$

The position has the same mass as the électron, but a positive charge.

Equation (3) depicts the transmutation of sodium-23 into magnesium-23

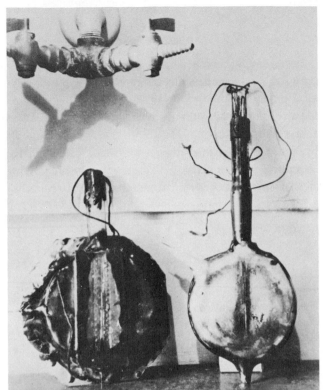

Fig. 17-2. The first two cyclotrons, (top picture) built by E. O. Lawrence and N. E. Edlefsen in 1930. They are about six inches in diameter. The lower picture shows the 184-inch cyclotron at the Radiation Laboratory, Berkeley, California.

by proton bombardment, and the net result of equation (4) is the addition of a neutron to the lithium nucleus to produce the isotope with the next higher mass number.

A useful theory concerning the *mechanism* of nuclear reactions assumes that they take place in two steps. In the first step, the incident particle is absorbed by the target nucleus to form a *compound nucleus.* This compound nucleus is of course very unstable and immediately breaks down into the final products. Using this theory, the mechanism of reaction (1) may be depicted as follows:

$$_2He^4 \; + \; _7N^{14} \longrightarrow \; [_9F^{18}] \longrightarrow \; _8O^{17} \; + \; _1H^1$$

projectile   target   unstable   products
                           compound
                           nucleus

Similarly, the mechanism of reaction (3) may be depicted as:

$$_1H^1 \; + \; _{11}Na^{23} \longrightarrow \; [_{12}Mg^{24}] \longrightarrow \; _{12}Mg^{23} \; + \; _0n^1$$

projectile   target   unstable   products
                           compound
                           nucleus

In certain nuclear transmutations the nucleus is left in a state of high energy, in which case this excess energy may be disposed of by the emission of a gamma ray. This is strongly reminiscent of the situation involving the orbital electrons of excited or energetic atoms which also rid themselves of their excess energy by the emission of radiation (See pages 108–109).

Nuclear Energy

A sample of a highly radioactive substance is capable of heating itself to a temperature appreciably above its surroundings. If the isotope is long-lived, it will continue to do this for a very long time. Thus, a gram of radium-226 over a period of one year will produce 1,000,000 calories of heat, and will continue to produce heat at a rate which diminishes only slowly for many centuries. What is the source of all this energy?

Again, if we compare the kinetic energy of the projectile and of the target nucleus with the kinetic energy of the *product nuclei,* we find that the kinetic energy of the products is frequently much greater than that of the starting materials. For example, in the reaction,

$$_3Li^7 + _1H^1 \longrightarrow \; _2He^4 + _2He^4$$

the proton must have a kinetic energy of 200,000 electron volts in order that the reaction may take place when the lithium atom is at rest (zero kinetic energy).* After the reaction has taken place, it is found that *each* of the $_2$He^4 nuclei has a kinetic energy of 8,700,000 ev, for a total of 17,400,000 ev. Subtracting the initial 200,000 ev we see that 17,200,000 ev of energy is produced for every lithium atom destroyed.

It is of interest to compare this amount of energy with the amounts of energy liberated in a typical *chemical* reaction. Thus, if water is formed by the combination of hydrogen and oxygen, the energy liberated for every molecule of water produced is only 3.0 ev, while in the nuclear reaction involving $_3$Li^7, 5,700,000 times as much energy is liberated per atom of lithium. It is generally the case that, whenever energy is liberated in a nuclear reaction, the amount liberated per nucleus reacted is of the order of millions of times greater than the amount liberated per molecule reacted in an ordinary chemical reaction. Again we may ask, what is the source of all this energy?

The answer to this question is to be found by a careful examination of the *masses* of particles involved in the nuclear reactions. To this point in the discussion, the masses of the nuclear particles and of the nuclei themselves have been rounded off to the nearest whole number, which was called the "mass number." In point of fact, the masses of the proton, neutron, and the various isotopes of each of the elements are known with considerable accuracy, and they are not integral numbers. When we consider these accurate masses, a very startling fact becomes apparent. For example, while the mass numbers in the reaction

$$_1H^1 + {_3}Li^7 \longrightarrow {_2}He^4 + {_2}He^4 + \text{kinetic energy}$$

add up to *eight* on both sides of the equation, a discrepancy is noticed when the *accurate masses* are used.

	$_1H^1$	+	$_3Li^7$	$\longrightarrow$	$_2He^4$	+	$_2He^4$
Accurate mass:	1.00815		7.01822		4.00388		4.00388

The masses on the left add up to 8.02637, while on the right the masses of the two helium nuclei add up to 8.00776. Thus, there is a discrepancy of 0.01861 mass units. In other words, during the course of this nuclear transformation, 0.01861 units of mass have disappeared, in violation of the law

---

* The *electron volt* (ev) is a convenient unit for expressing the energy involved in nuclear reactions. It is the amount of energy acquired by an electron when accelerated through a potential difference of one volt. One electron volt per particle is equivalent to 23,053 calories per mole of particles.

of conservation of mass! The present example is not an isolated one. In every case where energy is released in a nuclear reaction, it is found that the mass of the products is somewhat less than the mass of the reactants. It would seem that the law of conservation of mass does not apply to nuclear reactions.

Long before these experimental facts were known, Albert Einstein had supplied us with a possible explanation. In connection with his special theory of relativity, he had come to the conclusion that mass and energy are not independent entities, but that the mass of a body is actually a measure of its energy. Thus, when a body loses energy, its mass must decrease by a proportionate amount. The relationship that Einstein suggested in 1905 is given by the now well-known equation,

$$E = mc^2$$

where E represents the quantity of energy, m the amount of mass equivalent to that energy, and c^2 is the square of the velocity of light. Since m is multiplied by c^2, which is a *very* large number (expressed in familiar units, the velocity of light is 186,000 mi/sec), it is clear that a very large amount of energy is equivalent to even a very tiny amount of matter. Using this equation we can calculate that the complete conversion of one atomic mass unit of matter (1.66×10^{-24} g) will result in the release of 931 million electron volts (Mev) of energy. Employing this relationship, let us see if the mass

Albert Einstein: 1879–1955

discrepancy in the $_3\text{Li}^7$ reaction previously discussed can be accounted for in terms of the kinetic energy liberated in the reaction:

Let X = the energy equivalent to 0.01861 mass units, the mass discrepancy in this reaction. Since 931 Mev is equivalent to 1 mass unit, by simple proportion we have that

$$\frac{931 \text{ Mev}}{1 \text{ mass unit}} = \frac{X \text{ Mev}}{0.01861 \text{ mass units}}$$

Solving for X, we find that:

$$X = 931 \times 0.01861$$
$$X = 17.3 \text{ Mev}$$

This answer very nearly equals the 17.2 Mev of kinetic energy observed experimentally. Such good agreement would seem to confirm the correctness of Einstein's equation.

A cluster of protons and neutrons is a stable nucleus only if the total energy of the cluster is less than the total energy of the separated particles. In view of Einstein's equation, this means that the mass of the nucleus must be less than that of the separated protons and neutrons of which it is composed. This is always the case. Consider, for example, the formation of a helium nucleus from two protons and two neutrons:

$$2 \,_1\text{H}^1 \quad + \quad 2 \,_0\text{n}^1 \quad \longrightarrow \quad _2\text{He}^4$$

Accurate mass: 2×1.00815 $\quad 2 \times 1.00899$ $\quad\quad 4.00388$

The combined mass of the two protons and two neutrons is 4.03428, whereas the mass of the helium nucleus is only 4.00388. Thus there is a decrease in mass, and hence of energy, equivalent to 0.03040 mass units, or 28.3 Mev.

This energy, which is given up when the helium nucleus is formed, is called the *binding energy* since it is a measure of the tenacity with which the nuclear particles adhere to one another in the nucleus. Thus, if we wish to separate a helium nucleus into two protons and two neutrons, we must supply exactly this amount of energy.

It is of interest to calculate the average binding energy *per nuclear particle,* that is, the total binding energy divided by the total number of protons and neutrons. For helium, this quantity is 28.3 ÷ 4, or 7.08 Mev. For other nuclei, the average binding energy per nuclear particle may of course be different. For example, for bismuth-209, the average binding energy is found to be 7.8 Mev per nuclear particle, indicating that the nuclear particles are bound more firmly in this nucleus than in the helium nucleus. A plot of the average binding energy per nuclear particle for the various stable isotopes is given in Figure 17-3. Examination of this figure shows that the most stable nuclei, that is, those with the greatest binding energy per particle, are to be found in the mass number range 40–120 (corresponding to the elements of atomic number 20 to 50).

Figure 17-3 provides some insight into why the elements of high atomic weight are radioactive, and particularly why they usually decay by alpha emission. It can be seen from the figure that the binding energy per nuclear particle is relatively low for the very heavy elements. Thus, any process which converts a heavy nucleus to one of intermediate atomic weight and consequently greater binding energy will be favored. Such a conversion is accomplished by the loss of an alpha particle, which lowers the atomic mass by four units. It is usually an alpha particle that is lost simply because this is an especially stable light particle, as can also be seen from Figure 17-3.

In view of the large amounts of energy released in the nuclear reactions discussed in this section, one might think that these reactions could be employed for the commercial production of nuclear energy. However, there are two reasons why they are not. First, one must expend large amounts of energy in accelerating the projectiles to the required velocity; and second, in view of the small size of the nucleus, only a small fraction of the accelerated projectiles actually collide with a nucleus and react. As a result,

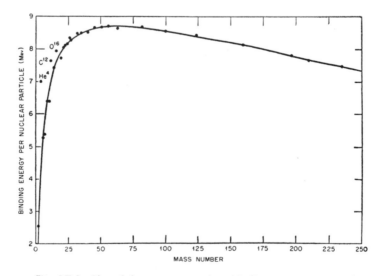

Fig. 17-3. Plot of the average nuclear binding energy per particle as a function of nuclear mass number. See S. Glasstone, *Source Book on Atomic Energy*, 2nd Ed. (D. Van Nostrand, 1958) page 351.

Enrico Fermi: 1901–1954

Fermi is noted both for his theories of nuclear reactions, and for his experimental studies of neutron-induced nuclear reactions. He directed the construction of the first nuclear chain reactor.

the energy used up in accelerating a large number of particles greatly exceeds the energy released in the relatively few reactions which occur.

Nuclear Fission

There is, however, a nuclear reaction which does not require that the bombarding particles be accelerated, and which can be made to be a prolific source of energy. As a consequence of earlier work by the Italian physicist, Enrico Fermi, directed toward the production of elements with atomic numbers greater than that of uranium, the German scientists, Otto Hahn and Fritz Strassmann, in 1938 bombarded samples of uranium with neutrons. In addition to the hoped-for heavier elements, they discovered that their sample, after bombardment, also contained atoms of the lighter element, barium, and of other elements with atomic numbers considerably *less* than that of uranium. At the time of their experiments, there was no known nuclear reaction mechanism which could account for the production of these nuclei from uranium. However, soon thereafter (1939), two other Germans, Lise Meitner and Otto Frisch, offered an explanation for these observations which is quite consistent with the experimental facts. They suggested that, instead of the usual small fragments being ejected during the nuclear reaction, the uranium nucleus was split in two by the incident neutron. Thus they envisioned that such elements as barium and krypton might be produced by the following mechanism:

$$_0n^1 + {}_{92}U^{235} \longrightarrow [{}_{92}U^{236}]$$

unstable compound nucleus

$$[{}_{92}U^{236}] \longrightarrow {}_{56}Ba^{143} + {}_{36}Kr^{90} + 3\ _0n^1$$

It is now known that many different isotopes, ranging in mass number from 72 to 160, are produced in the fission process. Some other examples of the many different ways in which the uranium nucleus may split are shown in the following equations:

$$[{}_{92}U^{236}] \longrightarrow {}_{54}Xe^{139} + {}_{38}Sr^{95} + 2\ _0n^1$$

$$[{}_{92}U^{236}] \longrightarrow {}_{53}I^{135} + {}_{39}Y^{97} + 4\ _0n^1$$

Examination of these equations shows that, in addition to the two principal fragments, each fission leads to the formation of several neutrons.

The energy released in such a process is about 200 Mev, or more than ten times as much as is released in typical nuclear reactions not involving fission. The release of such a large amount of energy is, of course, accompanied by a corresponding decrease in mass. The total mass of fission products plus neutrons is about 0.215 atomic mass units less than the mass of the uranium atom plus the incident neutron.

Consideration of Figure 17-3 provides an explanation for this nuclear breakdown with the release of large amounts of energy. The very heavy nuclei have a lower average binding energy than those of intermediate mass number. Therefore the heavy nuclei will, if possible, undergo conversion to the more stable intermediate elements with the release of energy. This energy is in the form of kinetic energy of the fission fragments, plus some radioactive decay energy, since the fission fragments themselves are usually radioactive. There is also considerable gamma radiation, which is released at the instant the fission takes place. Eventually most of this energy is converted to heat.

Since each fission requires only one neutron but produces several (2.5 neutrons on the average), the possibility exists that these product neutrons can go on to cause the fission of additional uranium-235 nuclei. When this happens, a branching chain reaction results, as shown schematically in Figure 17-4.

It is now history, of course, that such a chain reaction was first achieved in 1942 by a group of scientists at the University of Chicago, working under the direction of Enrico Fermi. They constructed a nuclear reactor consisting of lumps of uranium and uranium oxide embedded in a lattice of graphite. Under these conditions the rate of the fission process can be controlled, and energy is released at a rate slow enough to permit the use of

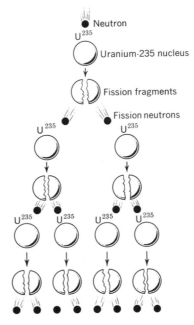

Fig. 17-4. Schematic representation of a branching nuclear chain reaction.

the reactor as a source of power. In the so-called "atomic" bomb (fission bomb), a large number of fissions occur *very* rapidly with an explosive release of energy.

Nuclear Fusion

An examination of Figure 17-3 reveals that the elements of *low* atomic number are also less stable than those of intermediate atomic number, just as those of high atomic number are unstable with respect to the intermediate group of elements. We have seen that under certain circumstances the very heavy elements can be split to produce elements of intermediate weight with the accompanying release of prodigious quantities of energy. In a similar fashion we would expect that it might be possible to *fuse* the nuclei of some of the lighter elements to form intermediate elements of greater stability, and that this process, too, would lead to the release of great amounts of energy. It has long been postulated that fusion reactions of just this type are the source of the sun's energy. In 1952 the fusion reaction was achieved by artificial means in what is commonly called the "hydrogen bomb." In this particular device an ordinary fission bomb is used to raise the temperature of the reacting nuclei to millions of degrees, at which temperature they have sufficient kinetic energy to fuse when they collide. The fusion reaction releases energy at the rate of from 3 to 20 Mev per fusion event. A number of examples of fusion reactions follow:

$$_1H^2 + {}_1H^2 \longrightarrow {}_2He^3 + {}_0n^1$$
$$_1H^2 + {}_1H^2 \longrightarrow {}_1H^3 + {}_1H^1$$
$$_1H^3 + {}_1H^2 \longrightarrow {}_2He^4 + {}_0n^1$$

Since there are estimated to be some 10^{17} pounds of deuterium ($_1H^2$) in the waters of the earth, and each pound is equivalent in energy to about 2500 *tons* of coal, it is quickly appreciated that a controlled fusion reactor would provide a virtually inexhaustible supply of energy. A great effort is being made today to build such a reactor, and there is every reason to hope that success may not be too far in the future.

Suggestions for Further Reading

W. Panofsky, "The Linear Accelerator," *Scientific American*, Oct. 1954, p. 40.

R. R. Wilson, "Particle Accelerators," *Scientific American*, March 1958, p. 64.

I. Perlman and G. T. Seaborg, "The Synthetic Elements," *Scientific American*, April 1950, p. 38.

A. Ghiorso and G. T. Seaborg, "The Newest Synthetic Elements," *Scientific American*, Dec. 1956, p. 64.

E. P. Ney, "Heavy Elements from Space," *Scientific American*, May 1951, p. 26.

O. Hahn, "The Discovery of Fission," *Scientific American*, Feb. 1958, p. 76.

H. A. Bethe, "What Holds the Nucleus Together?" *Scientific American*, Sept. 1953, p. 58.

R. F. Post, "Fusion Power," *Scientific American*, Dec. 1957, p. 73.

G. Burbridge and F. Hoyle, "Anti-Matter," *Scientific American*, April 1958, p. 34.

G. Wendt, *You and the Atom* (New York: Whiteside, Inc., and William Morrow & Company, Inc., 1956).

L. Fermi, *Atoms in the Family* (Chicago: University of Chicago Press, 1953).

A. H. Compton, *Atomic Quest* (New York: Oxford University Press, 1956).

E. E. Levinger, *Albert Einstein* (New York: J. Messner, Inc., 1949).

I. B. Cohen, "An Interview with Einstein," *Scientific American*, July 1955, p. 68.

N. Bohr and I. I. Rabi, "Albert Einstein," *Scientific American*, June 1955, p. 31.

Appendix A

Some scientific units

Mass. The standard unit of mass is the *kilogram* (kg), roughly 2.2 pounds. The *international prototype kilogram* is a metal cylinder fabricated from a corrosion-resistant platinum-iridium alloy and is preserved at the International Bureau of Weights and Measures in Sèvres, France. One gram (g) is equal to one-thousandth of a kilogram.

Weight. The weight of an object is a measure of how strongly the object is attracted by the earth. The unit of weight has been defined so that, at the earth's surface, an object with a mass of one gram also has a weight of one gram. In other words, the definition of the unit of weight is such that for most practical purposes, the terms mass and weight may be used interchangeably.

Length. The standard unit of length is the *meter* (m), equivalent to 1.0936 yards or 39.37 inches. The *international prototype meter* is the distance between two lines engraved on a platinum-iridium bar, kept at 0°C, currently on deposit at the International Bureau of Weights and Measures. The original intention was to define one meter as 1/40,000,000 of the mean circumference of the earth, but owing to error the international prototype meter is actually closer to 1/40,009,000 of the earth's mean circumference.

A convenient derived unit is the centimeter (cm) which is equal to one-hundredth of a meter. One centimeter is roughly equivalent to 0.4 inch.

Volume. The unit of volume in the metric system is the *cubic centimeter* (cc), which is the volume of a cube 1 cm on each side. One cubic centimeter is equal to 0.0010567 quart, or roughly one-thousandth of a quart.

Another unit of volume employed in scientific work is the *liter* (l), which is the volume occupied by 1 kg of water at 4°C. A derived unit is the milliliter (ml), or one-thousandth of a liter. One milliliter is so nearly equal to one cubic centimeter (1 ml = 1.000027 cc) that the two units are almost always used interchangeably.

Time. The primary standard in the measurement of time is the mean solar day, which consists of 24 hours or 86,400 seconds. In scientific work, it is customary to express time intervals in *seconds* (sec).

Temperature. In scientific work, the centigrade scale of temperature is used. On this scale, the melting point of ice is defined as 0°, and the boiling point of water at a pressure of 1 atm as 100°. The interval between melting and boiling points is therefore divided into one hundred equal units, each called one degree centigrade (1°C). In practice, temperatures are measured by means of a substance, some convenient property of which varies with the temperature. The most commonly used thermometer is made of liquid mercury sealed in a glass tube. An increase in temperature causes an elongation of the mercury column.

The familiar household thermometer employs the Fahrenheit scale. On this scale, ice melts at 32°, and water boils at 212°. Normal body temperature is 98.6° on the Fahrenheit scale—37.0° on the centigrade scale. To convert from one scale to the other, the following equations are used:

$$(°F) = \frac{9}{5}(°C) + 32$$

$$(°C) = \frac{5}{9}[(°F) - 32]$$

Appendix B

Exponential notation

THE NUMBERS encountered in the study of chemistry are often very large or very small. The usual decimal notations become cumbersome when dealing with such very large or very small numbers, and it is convenient to use a more compact exponential notation.

The reader will recall that:

$$100 = 10 \times 10 \quad \text{or } 10^2 \text{ (two zeros)}$$
$$1000 = 10 \times 10 \times 10 \quad \text{or } 10^3 \text{ (three zeros)}$$
$$1{,}000{,}000 = 10 \times 10 \times 10 \times 10 \times 10 \times 10 \quad \text{or } 10^6 \text{ (six zeros)}$$

and so forth. In using exponential notation, the unwieldy number is rewritten so that only one digit appears to the left of the decimal point, and the new number is then multiplied by 10 raised to the correct power. For example, if the population of a city is 8,200,000 people, we may first rewrite this number as $8.2 \times 1{,}000{,}000$, so that only one digit (the eight) appears to the left of the decimal point. Next the number 1,000,000 is written in exponential form as 10^6, and we obtain the result:

$$8{,}200{,}000 = 8.2 \times 10^6$$

To use an example from the field of chemistry, there are known to be 602,000,000,000,000,000,000,000 molecules in one gram molecular weight. Obviously, this number is written more easily and apprehended more readily in the exponential form: 6.02×10^{23}.

The same rule applies for very small numbers, but now the exponent is negative. The reader will recall that:

$$0.1 = 10^{-1}$$
$$0.01 = 10^{-2}$$
$$0.001 = 10^{-3}$$

and so forth. Thus, if the diameter of an atom is known to be 0.000,000,030 cm, we first write this number as $3.0 \times 0.000{,}000{,}010$ cm, and finally in exponential notation as 3.0×10^{-8} cm.

Appendix C

Glossary of scientific terms

ADSORPTION—the binding of molecules onto the surfaces of substances.

ALPHA PARTICLE—subatomic particle of mass 4 and charge $+2$; the helium nucleus.

ATOM—fundamental building block of matter; atoms combine to form molecules.

ATOMIC MASS NUMBER—atomic weight of an isotope, rounded off to the nearest integer.

ATOMIC NUMBER—the net positive charge on the *nucleus* of an atom; equal to the number of *protons* in the nucleus.

ATOMIC WEIGHT—the ratio of the weight of a sample of the element to that of a sample of oxygen containing an equal number of atoms, on a scale on which the atomic weight of oxygen is 16.000.

AVOGADRO'S NUMBER—the number of molecules in one gram molecular weight; 6.02×10^{23}.

BETA PARTICLE—an *electron* emitted by the nucleus of an atom in the process of radioactive decay.

BOND—the link joining two atoms in a molecule.

BROWNIAN MOTION—the irregular zig-zag motion of tiny particles suspended in a liquid, owing to the impacts of molecules of the liquid on these particles.

CALORIE (gram calorie)—a unit of energy; the amount of heat required to raise the temperature of one gram of water from $14.5°C$ to $15.5°C$.

CATALYST—a substance, other than a reactant, added to a chemical reaction in order to change its rate.

CATHODE RAY—a beam of high-speed electrons emitted by the cathode (negative electrode) in a vacuum tube.

CIS—*see* isomer, geometrical.

COMPOUND—a pure substance formed by the chemical combination of two or more elements.

CONDUCTIVITY, electrical—a measure of the ability of a substance to allow the passage of an electric current.

COSMIC RAYS—a highly penetrating type of radiation coming from outer space.

DENSITY—mass per unit volume of a substance.

232

ELECTRIC CHARGE—charge acquired by a body when it gains or loses electrons.

ELECTROLYSIS—the decomposition of a compound through the agency of an electric current.

ELEMENT—a pure substance which cannot be decomposed by chemical means.

ELECTROMAGNETIC RADIATION—a radiation emitted by oscillating electric charges; the *frequency* of the oscillation determines the nature of the radiation; in order of increasing frequency, the types of electromagnetic radiation are radio waves, infrared, visible, ultraviolet, and X-rays or gamma rays.

ELECTRON VOLT—a unit of energy; the energy of an electron when accelerated through a potential difference of one volt.

ELECTRON—a subatomic particle having a mass of 1/1840 of the mass of the hydrogen atom and a charge of -1.

EXPONENT—the number n in the expression x^n, which indicates that x is repeated as a factor n times.

FORMULA—in chemistry, a graphical way of representing on paper the structure and composition of molecules. The *molecular formula* gives only the numbers of atoms of different kinds in one molecule; the *structural formula* shows also the manner in which the atoms are linked; the *geometrical formula* describes their arrangement in space.

FREQUENCY—the number of occurrences of an event in unit time.

GAMMA RAYS—*electromagnetic radiation* of very high frequency emitted by the nuclei of atoms undergoing radioactive decay.

GRAM ATOMIC WEIGHT—the weight of 6.02×10^{23} atoms of a given element; numerically equivalent to the atomic weight expressed in grams.

GRAM MOLECULAR VOLUME—the volume occupied by one gram molecular weight of any gaseous compound at $0°C$ and 1 atm pressure; about 22.4 liters.

GRAM MOLECULAR WEIGHT—the weight of 6.02×10^{23} molecules of a given compound; numerically equivalent to the molecular weight expressed in grams.

HETEROGENEOUS—refers to a sample of matter of nonuniform composition.

HOMOGENEOUS—refers to a sample of matter which is uniform throughout.

INSULATOR, electrical—a substance which does not readily conduct electric current.

ION—an electrically charged atom or molecule.

ISOMERS—two structurally different molecules having the same molecular formula. *Structural isomers* are molecules with the same molecular formula but different structural formulas. *Geometrical isomers* are molecules with the same structural formula but different geometrical formulas. The *cis*-isomer has two identical groups or atoms on the same side of the double bond; the *trans*-isomer has the identical groups on opposite sides of the double bond.

ISOTOPES—two atoms of the same element (having the same atomic number) with different atomic weights.

KINETIC ENERGY—the energy possessed by a body by virtue of its motion.

LATTICE, crystal—an orderly three-dimensional array of atoms, ions, or molecules. (See page 64.)

LAW, scientific—a generalization, based on experiments or observations, summarizing some phenomenon of nature or natural mode of behavior. Laws are expressions of our factual knowledge and are not to be confused with *theories*.

MASS NUMBER—*see* atomic mass number.

MOLE—same as *gram molecular weight*.

MOLECULAR FORMULA—*see* formula.

MOLECULAR WEIGHT—the sum of the atomic weights of the constituent atoms in the molecule.

MOLECULES—the smallest particles into which a pure substance may be subdivided, the collection of which still has the same properties as the original sample.

NEUTRON—a subatomic particle of *mass number* one and zero charge.

PHASE—a homogeneous, physically distinct portion of matter; e.g., the liquid phase, the gas phase.

POSITRON—a subatomic particle having the same mass as the *electron*, but a charge of $+1$.

POTENTIAL ENERGY—the energy possessed by a body due to its interaction with other bodies.

PROTON—a subatomic particle of *mass number* one and a charge of $+1$.

REFRACTIVE INDEX—a measure of the speed at which light travels in the given sample of matter.

SYNTHESIS—the art or process of making or building up a compound.

THEORY—a convenient model, designed to explain a set of related observations or phenomena.

TRANS—*see* isomer, geometrical.

Questions and problems

Chapter 1

Read Appendix A before answering questions 1–4.

1. In what units of the metric system would the *magnitude* of the following items be most appropriately expressed?
   (a) The thickness of a book.
   (b) The volume of water in one cup.
   (c) The volume of a room.
   (d) The speed of an airplane in flight.
   (e) The distance from the earth to the moon.
2. To what centigrade temperature does 77° Fahrenheit correspond?
3. Convert 155°C to degrees Fahrenheit.
4. Calculate the postage (International Airmail) for a letter weighing 2⅛ ounces, if airmail costs 10¢ for each ten grams or fraction thereof.
5. What are the most important characteristics of the "scientific attitude?"
6. In what ways are submicroscopic models useful to the scientist?

Chapter 2

1. Explain how best to separate or purify each of the following mixtures into its components:
   (a) A mixture of sand and sugar.
   (b) A solution of alcohol in water.
   (c) Impure Epsom salts.
   (d) A mixture of substances extracted from liver.
2. What is meant by the term "property"? How are the properties of substances used for their identification?
3. What are the characteristics of a pure substance?
4. Contrast "operational definition" with "Aristotelian definition."
5. What are the general characteristics of each of the three states of matter?
6. Why is it desirable to isolate a substance in the pure form before studying its properties?
7. Give an example of:
   (a) A solid solution.
   (b) A liquid solution.
   (c) A gaseous solution.

Chapter 3

1. Decide whether each of the following items refers to an element, compound, or mixture. State your reasons for each decision.
   (a) Different samples of the given material differ in their composition.
   (b) Physical properties of all samples are identical.
   (c) The sample cannot be altered by many attempts at decomposition.
   (d) The substance can be formed from a number of other substances by chemical reaction.

2. Decide which of the following is an element, a compound, or a mixture. On what evidence are these decisions based? (a) Cement. (b) Ink. (c) Air. (d) Gold. (e) Water. (f) Milk.

3. Which of the following are physical and which are chemical changes?
   (a) Boiling of water.
   (b) Dissolving of salt in water.
   (c) Butter becoming rancid.
   (d) Burning of wood.
   (e) Cooking of an egg.

4. What are the *macroscopic* characteristics of all chemical changes?

5. Suggest three general ways in which chemical reactions may be brought about. Describe the apparatus in which these operations could be carried out.

Chapter 4

1. A sample of pure potassium chlorate, weighing 3.00 g, on heating liberates 1.17 g of pure oxygen. Calculate the per cent by weight of oxygen in the compound, potassium chlorate.

2. Berzelius found that 10.0 g of iron reacts with 5.87 g of sulfur to form a compound. Calculate the weight per cent of iron in this compound.

3. Iron and chlorine form two compounds, one containing 44.0% iron and the other 34.4% iron. Calculate the ratio of the weights of chlorine in combination with 100 g of iron in each of the two compounds.

4. The elements sodium and oxygen will form two possible compounds, sodium oxide and sodium peroxide. Sodium oxide consists of 74.2% sodium and 25.8% oxygen. On the basis of the law of multiple proportions, suggest a possible composition for sodium peroxide.

5. How would you establish experimentally the law of conservation of mass?

6. How does the atomic theory of John Dalton explain:
   (a) The law of definite composition?
   (b) The law of multiple proportions?

7. What are some of the shortcomings of Dalton's theory?
8. Differentiate between a law and a theory, and explain the purpose for which each is employed.

Chapter 5

1. Why can energy be regarded as a physical property of a substance?
2. Under what conditions will any change take place spontaneously? Give two examples of changes which you would expect to occur spontaneously.
3. Under what conditions will the total energy of a moving object remain constant?
4. For the following changes indicate what, if any, change occurs in the energy of the system. Also indicate the form of energy in question.
   (a) Liquid alcohol is converted to alcohol vapor.
   (b) A rock, initially at rest, falls to the ground and again comes to rest.
   (c) An automobile is accelerated from rest to 40 mi/hr on level ground.
   (d) One gram of carbon is converted to carbon dioxide.
   (e) Water is converted to hydrogen and oxygen.
   (f) A block of iron is heated from 25°C to 500°C.
5. Consider two bodies, which attract one another, separated by a very great distance. What is the potential energy of the system at this distance? What happens to the potential energy as the two bodies come closer together? What can you say about the potential energy when the two bodies are touching one another?
6. Consider the same problem for two bodies that repel one another.

Chapter 6

1. If the temperature of a gas is increased, what can be said about the average kinetic energy of the molecules of the gas?
2. If a number of different gases in different vessels are all at the same temperature, what can be said about the average velocities of the molecules of the different gases?
3. How could one reduce the pressure that a gas exerts on the walls of its container?
4. Describe the nature of the solid and liquid states in terms of the kinetic theory. What are the *submicroscopic* effects of changing temperature and pressure on each of these states?
5. What happens to the internal energy of a gas as (a) the pressure, (b) the temperature, is increased?

Chapter 7

1. A compound composed of the elements X and Y contains, on analysis, 50 weight per cent of X and 50 weight per cent of Y. Assume that each X atom weighs half as much as a Y atom. Calculate a possible molecular formula for the compound.
2. The compound MZ_2 on analysis is found to contain 27.2 weight per cent of M. Calculate the relative weight of atoms M and Z.
3. One volume of nitrogen gas reacts with three volumes of chlorine gas to give two volumes of a gaseous product. Calculate from these data the molecular formula of the compound, assuming that all volumes were measured at the same temperature and pressure.
4. What is the molecular weight of a gas, if 11.2 liters of it weighs 28.9 g when measured at 0°C and 1 atm. pressure?
5. Using standard atomic weights, calculate the gram molecular weights of the following compounds: (a) CH_2O. (b) C_7H_{14}. (c) $AlCl_3$. (d) H_2SO_4.
6. Calculate the number of atoms in a drop of pure water (0.05 g).
7. Calculate the weight of one atom of chlorine.

Chapter 8

1. What is the total weight of all the electrons in one gram atom of gold?
2. Describe a method for establishing the sign of the charge of a stream of particles produced in a cathode-ray tube.
3. What evidence is there that electrons are a common constituent of all matter?
4. What experiments were crucial in establishing the inadequacy of the Daltonian atom? What modifications were required as a consequence?
5. What are the particles produced by the ionization of hydrogen gas in a cathode-ray tube?
6. Is Dalton's theory wrong? If so, why? If not, why not?

Chapter 9

1. What are the principal differences between the Bohr theory and the Rutherford theory of the hydrogen atom?
2. What was Bohr's justification for ignoring the laws of macroscopic electrodynamics?
3. How is the "spacing" (energy difference) between the various electron orbits of the hydrogen atom determined experimentally?

4. What is the radius of the fifth Bohr orbit? What is the energy of an electron in this orbit, and how many times does the electron complete a circuit of this orbit in one second?

5. How many hydrogen atoms, all in the first excited state ($n = 2$), could be placed side-by-side in a row 1 cm long?

6. What are some of the processes that can lead to the excitation of a hydrogen atom?

7. What is a quantum?

Chapter 10

1. Decide, with the aid of a periodic chart, whether or not stable compounds with the following formulas exist: (a) SrSe. (b) CsI_2. (c) PN. (d) Ca_3Al_2. (e) TeHe.

2. An unknown element, X, is known by its reactions to be a member of the oxygen family. The compound of X with cesium contains 32.5 weight per cent of X. What is the most probable atomic weight of X?

3. How would you decide, experimentally, whether two elements belong to the same family of elements?

4. Explain why it is unlikely that any new elements with atomic numbers less than 102 will ever be discovered.

5. Distinguish between the "rows" and "columns" of the periodic chart.

6. How many elements are there in each of the first five periods of the periodic chart?

Chapter 11

1. List the number of electrons in
   (a) The first shell of the uranium atom.
   (b) The second shell of the boron atom.
   (c) The outermost shell of the bromine atom.
   (d) The fourth shell of the magnesium atom.
   (e) The fifth shell of the xenon atom.

2. Draw orbital diagrams such as those shown on page 137 for the following atoms: (a) Chlorine. (b) Nitrogen. (c) Nickel. (d) Germanium.

3. What is the main distinction between orbits and orbitals?

4. Why is it not possible to draw the exact boundaries of the various electron orbitals?

5. In some versions of the periodic chart, the column containing the inert gases is headed by the number 0 instead of VIII. Criticize this practice.

Chapter 12

1. Why is it possible to ignore the electrons of inner shells when considering compound formation?
2. In general, what kinds of elements are most likely to enter into the formation of ionic compounds?
3. Write electron-dot formulas of the ions most likely to be formed from the reactions of the following elements:
   (a) Beryllium and fluorine.
   (b) Calcium and selenium.
   (c) Rubidium and oxygen.
4. What are the chief physical characteristics of typical ionic compounds? Explain these properties in terms of the mode of bonding employed in their formation.
5. What would you expect to be the products if the following ionic compounds (the molten salts) were subjected to electrolysis? (a) CsI. (b) $CaBr_2$. (c) KF.
6. Explain why it is not possible to specify the molecular weight of an ionic compound.

Chapter 13

1. Write plausible electron-dot formulas for the following covalent molecules: (a) HOCl. (b) N_2H_4. (c) CH_2O. (d) C_2HBr. (e) C_3H_8. (f) H_2SO_4.
2. Contrast the physical and chemical properties of covalent compounds with those of ionic compounds, and explain the differences in terms of the differences in the mode of bonding.
3. Under what conditions can a covalent bond be formed between two atoms?
4. Under what conditions is it possible for single, double, or triple bonds to form between two atoms?
5. What types of elements are likely to form covalent compounds?
6. The melting point of chloroform (CH_3Cl) is $-64°C$. Are the bonds ionic or covalent? Draw an electron-dot structure for this compound.
7. How would you determine whether a high-melting solid is an ionic or a covalent compound?

Chapter 14

1. For each of the following molecular formulas write two isomeric structural formulas that satisfy the octet rule: (a) C_2H_6S. (b) C_5H_{12}. (c) C_3H_8O. (d) C_3H_6. (e) C_4H_8.

2. Which of the following molecules can exhibit geometrical isomerism?

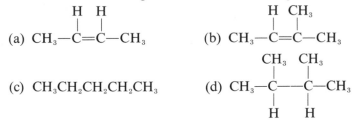

(a) $CH_3-C=C-CH_3$ (with H, H above)

(b) $CH_3-C=C-CH_3$ (with H, CH_3 above)

(c) $CH_3CH_2CH_2CH_2CH_3$

(d) $CH_3-C---C-CH_3$ (with CH_3, CH_3 above and H, H below)

3. Explain why you would expect to find two isomeric compounds with the molecular formula CH_2Cl_2 if the four bonds of the carbon atom were directed towards the corners of a square.

4. What are the structural requirements for optical isomerism?

5. Describe in a general way how one makes assignments of structural formulas to actual substances.

6. To what does the term "tetrahedral carbon atom" refer?

Chapter 15

1. Consider a chemical reaction, the rate of which is determined by the collision of two molecules. What will be the effect on the rate of each of the following?
   (a) Increasing the concentration of the reactants.
   (b) Lowering the temperature.
   (c) Increasing the pressure.
   (d) Increasing the size of the vessel.
   (e) Stirring, if the reaction mixture is not homogeneous.
   (f) Adding a catalyst.

2. What name best describes each of the following reactions?

   (a) $C_2H_2O_4 \longrightarrow CO + CO_2 + H_2O$

   (b) $C=C + Zn \longrightarrow H-C\equiv C-H + ZnBr_2$ (with H, Br above and Br, H below)

   (c) $NaI + H-C-Br \longrightarrow NaBr + H-C-I$ (each C with H above and H below)

   (d) $CH_2O_2 \longrightarrow CO + H_2O$

   (e) $HBr + H-C=C-H \longrightarrow H-C-C-Br$ (left C's with H above and H below; right with H, H above and H, H below)

3. Frequently a reaction in which the products have considerably less energy than the reactants nevertheless requires the addition of energy in order to get it started. Explain.

4. What submicroscopic factors determine the speed with which a chemical reaction will go?

Chapter 16

1. Consider the nucleus of the carbon-14 atom.
   (a) How many protons are in the nucleus of the atom? How many neutrons?
   (b) What is the mass number of this nucleus? What is the atomic number?
   (c) How many electrons are associated with the nucleus (in the neutral atom)?

2. Which of the following nuclei represents atoms of the same element?
   (a) 4p, 4n   (b) 4p, 5n   (c) 5p, 4n   (d) 3p, 5n   (e) 4p, 6n.

3. Which of the following nuclei would you expect to be unusually stable?
   (a) $_6C^{13}$ (b) $_{50}Sn^{112}$ (c) $_{20}Ca^{40}$ (d) $_{11}Na^{23}$.

4. What are our current ideas about the forces binding the various nuclear particles together to form a nucleus?

5. What is the experimental evidence that the nuclei of the atoms consist of protons and neutrons?

6. Which of the various nuclear detection devices discussed in the text gives the most information about nuclear reactions? In what way?

7. A sample of the element X consists of 21% of X^{92} and 79% of X^{94}. What is the chemical atomic weight of the sample?

Chapter 17

Complete the following nuclear reactions:

1. $_{88}Ra^{226} \longrightarrow {} _{86}Rn^{222} + $ ___?___

2. $_{63}Eu^{154} \longrightarrow {} _{64}Gd^{154} + $ ___?___

3. $_{62}Sm^{143} \longrightarrow {} _{61}Pm^{143} + $ ___?___

4. $_{92}U^{238} + $ ___?___ $\longrightarrow {} _{92}U^{239} \longrightarrow {} _{93}Np^{239} + $ ___?___

5. $_{29}Cu^{63} + $ ___?___ $\longrightarrow {} _{30}Zn^{63} + $ ___?___

6. $_{92}U^{236} \longrightarrow $ ___?___ $ + {} _{38}Sr^{95} + 4 {}_0n^1$

7. Thorium-225 has a half-life of 8 minutes. At the end of 24 minutes, what fraction of the original thorium-225 will still be present?

8. Under what circumstances will a nuclear reaction release energy?

9. Calculate the amount of energy which would be liberated if one gram of hydrogen were completely converted into energy.
10. Give examples of:
    (a) Fission.
    (b) Fusion.
    (c) Radioactive decay.

Index*

* See also Glossary of Scientific Terms, pp. 232–234.